FINDING DESIGNATED GROUND ZERO

Book II of the First Strike Series

THOMAS J. YEGGY

This is a work of fiction. Characters, places, and incidents are products of the author's imagination, are used fictitiously, and are not to be construed as real. Any resemblance to actual events, locations, organizations, or people, living or dead, is purely coincidental.

ISBN: 979-8-9878884-3-8 (Paperback)

ISBN: 979-8-9878884-4-5 (eBook)

For Clarence "Kelly" Johnson, Paul Croft,

Walter Yeggy, and John Grimsich

* * *

Lockheed employees who made our country safer

What is history but a fable agreed upon?

—Napoleon Bonaparte, 1816

ABOUT THE AUTHOR

Thomas J. Yeggy is a graduate of the University of Iowa College of Law and practiced law in Davenport, Iowa, and Rock Island, Illinois, for many years. He served as the mental health and substance abuse judge for Scott County, Iowa, for more than 25 years. In that position he developed a keen understanding of the difficulties that everyday life presents regardless of social or economic status. As a judge, he authored more than 1,500  opinions, and only one was reversed by the appellate courts. He was also a licensed Series 7 broker at Beyer & Company Investments in Davenport, Iowa, for more than two decades.

Yeggy's interest in the development and control of nuclear weapons goes back to images he once saw of the nuclear destruction of Hiroshima and Nagasaki. With his keen insight into the nature of mankind and their proclivity to use violence as a problem-solving mechanism, he wondered how we had made it through crisis after crisis without destroying ourselves. In 1992, when Robert McNamara stated that we had made it through the Cuban Missile Crisis with "just plain dumb luck," Yeggy decided to investigate just how lucky we have been. He explains what he found in this *First Strike* series. We have been very lucky, but it may not continue.

Yeggy currently resides in Pensacola Beach, Florida, with his wife, Eileen, and spends summers in Davenport with his grandchildren, Jeff and Ashley Brown. You can usually find Thomas and Eileen at Emeis Park in Davenport on a late summer afternoon running with their granddogs, Otis and Emme. The author's photo is from Fort Pickens Road in Pensacola Beach, courtesy of Eileen Yeggy.

AUTHOR'S NOTE

This book is a work of fiction, but much of the history is based on fact. During the Cold War, US civilian and military leaders often turned to the scientific community for answers to questions concerning the United States' vulnerability to a preemptive strike by the Soviet Union. Many scientists produced answers, laboring in obscurity in organizations such as the RAND Corporation. Other scientists produced essential reports such as the Lincoln Project and the Gaither Report. But there were also many so-called Caleb Youngs, our composite fictional character, in these and other scientific organizations, relegated to obscurity by mainstream historians who elevated others to fame beyond their contributions. This book and the others in this *First Strike* series are fictional insights into those in the scientific community who dedicated their lives to the defense of freedom. It is intended to put them in their proper place in history.

At the end of *Mushroom Cloud*, Book I in this series, Joseph Stalin was murdered at his Kuntsevo Dacha residence outside of Moscow by party leaders who had lost confidence in his ability to conduct a surprise attack on the United States. Dwight D. Eisenhower's administration achieved a détente with Nikita Khrushchev that Harry Truman could only have dreamed of, primarily because Khrushchev was perceptive enough to know that war with the West was out of the question, while Stalin was too sick to realize the potential devastation.

This book, *Designated Ground Zero*, Book II in this *First Strike* series, is dominated by Eisenhower's Massive Retaliation Doctrine and the development of the U-2 by Lockheed and the Technological Capabilities Panel (TCP). Despite killing many test pilots, the plane resulted in dispelling myths such as the bomber and missile gap that John F. Kennedy rode into the White House on.

Many events with their genesis in the mid- to late 1950s came to dominate American nuclear policy for many years to come. The development by the National Security Council of the top-secret Net Evaluation Subcommittee (NESC) in 1954, which "gamed" simulated wars between the United States and the Soviets, came to dominate American foreign policy and nuclear strategy for decades. Similarly, the Single Integrated Option Plan for 1962 (SIOP-62), developed by Eisenhower's Administration in late 1960 as a result of NESC reports, spawned Kennedy's Flexible Response Doctrine of the early 1960s.

The problem in the 1950s, even with critical information revealed by the U-2 flights, was that the Air Force and even the scientific community constantly overestimated Soviet capabilities. The Air Force's motive for the overestimation was simple—budget domination by their branch and an FSW-0 (First Strike Window O response). It was only through this method that the Strategic Air Command (SAC), guided by General Thomas S. Power and General Thomas D. White, was able to create SIOP-62, deploying 3,200 warheads and 7,847 megatons of nuclear bombs that would have resulted in 285 million deaths within days of launch. Civilian leaders pushed back.

Scientists such as George Kistiakowsky, George Rathjens, and Carl Kaysen questioned the seemingly massive obliteration of the 1,062 Designated Ground Zeros (DGZ). Scientists at the CIA had determined that SIOP-62 would also destroy the United States. They continued to enhance imaginary Soviet abilities to deter the US military from a first strike. The story continues.

Thomas J. Yeggy

PROLOGUE

March 5, 1953 – 1415 Hours
YMCA, Washington, DC

For Caleb Young, dominating the game was so routine that it almost wasn't fun anymore. His glory basketball days went way back, but now at the age of thirty-two, he was still making it rain from anywhere on the court. Some of the guys sharing the court with him that day had once played a little college ball, but not with any major team. Most of them were accountants, lawyers, and other mid-level bureaucrats who wanted to stave off abdominal bulge or the inevitable heart attack destined to strike almost anyone in government service.

Most of them were younger than Caleb, but it didn't matter. His understanding of the physics involved in basketball had given him an almost insurmountable advantage throughout his playing days. He had crossed paths with some impressive players in his day. After playing one day with Caleb, George Glamack, the 1940 and 1941 Helms Player of the Year from quaint little University of North Carolina in Chapel Hill, had toweled off and said, "If you'd come play for Bill Lange and the North Carolina Tar Heels against some real competition in the Southern Conference, you'd be an All-American. He's a great coach."

Caleb remembered two things about the day he was on the court with Glamack. First, he had just thoroughly abused him in five consecutive games. Second, he was too busy with his studies in particle physics at Princeton to take more than a recreational interest in basketball. "I already have a great coach," he told Glamack. He's the best in the field. His name is Dr. Albert Einstein."

Caleb's thoughts came back to the game and the young man who was guarding him too closely. Caleb had just made six set shots in a row, so the guy crowded him a little. He had his hand on Caleb's hip to keep him from going to his right. Caleb waited and watched the arm.

Caleb feinted right. His bicep tensed. He had him. Then he cross-stepped and drove to the basket. A stocky guy with slicked-back hair moved to cut him off, but Caleb left the floor and dropped the ball into the hoop. He had thought about dunking it, but there was no reason to showboat.

"That's game, fellas," Caleb announced. "Anyone want one more before we head back to the grind?"

The young man who'd been guarding Caleb said, "Only if I get to be on your team next time. You're wearing me out, old man."

Caleb was going to remind him that he was only thirty-two, but he spotted someone wearing a bespeckled suit hotfooting it across the hardwood. It was a messenger from the State Department.

"Dr. Young," he said. "This is for you."

Caleb broke the seal, read the note, and headed for the door. "Gotta go, fellas. See you next week." Caleb looked at the messenger. "Get my stuff from the locker room."

☙

Back in his office at the Central Intelligence Agency, Caleb took a French bath in the sink and changed into a spare suit. He sat and stared at the missive he'd received—these three words on a Telex destined to alter the entire course of history:

Stalin is dead.

1

April 1964 – 0830 Hours
Office of William Forde, Esq., Chief of
the Criminal Division and CIA Liaison
950 Pennsylvania Avenue, Suite 710
Washington, DC

"It was March 5th, 1953," Dr. Caleb Young testified. "A sprint ensued between Beria's state police and Khrushchev's army ground forces. Which one would gain control of Moscow and the Politburo was anyone's guess, but Beria didn't take any chances. While the other three conspirators stood by crying over Stalin's dead body and whispering their farewells, Beria raced away in his car."

William Forde stared at Caleb across the large table in his office. As Assistant U.S. Attorney and Chief of the Criminal Division, Forde usually knew what was going on in the world, but he seemed surprised at what Caleb was telling him. Since Caleb spoke primarily without notes, Forde wondered how accurate his memory was. Caleb couldn't figure out if Forde respected his knowledge or just considered him a pedantic academic. Maybe his look was one of contempt for what he considered just another spider in the expansive CIA web.

Caleb, this chief scientist for the CIA, had been interrogated for days now in hopes of finding out if the CIA had some disreputable involvement in the assassination of President John F. Kennedy. The questioning had begun just a month after Kennedy's death. Caleb didn't have any choice—U.S. Deputy Attorney General Nicholas Katzenbach had successfully gotten a subpoena from a grand jury to force Dr. Caleb Young to appear for this long, clandestine inquiry.

"Go on," Forde said. "I'm pretty sure how this turns out. But before you take off again on one of your long dissertations, let me give you my thoughts. Dr. Young, all my contacts— even Allen Dulles, the former Director—have debunked an assassination as a fairy tale. A plot to kill Stalin would have cost all of them their lives."

Caleb replied calmly. "I relied on facts that all your contacts lacked. I reached my conclusion based on my meetings with Colonel Penkovsky at the Peace Conferences. I relied on logical deductions based on Malenkov's and Khrushchev's comments denouncing Stalin. More importantly, they privately acknowledged that a war with the West would have resulted in the annihilation of the Soviet Union. And besides, they wouldn't be any more dead than if they had been incinerated by thermonuclear weapons."

The perplexed look on Forde's face encouraged Caleb to divulge the rest of the Agency's information.

"Let's go through a brief history of what went on in Moscow the day after Stalin was murdered," Caleb continued. "Here's what Enver Hoxha, the Premier of Albania, told one of our agents just last year." Caleb grabbed binder 59 and read from it.

On March 6th, 1953, the Central Committee of the Party, the Council of ministers, and the presidium of the Supreme Soviet of the USSR were summoned to an urgent joint meeting. On occasions of great losses such as the death of Stalin, urgent meetings are necessary and indispensable. However, the many important changes that were announced in the press one day later showed that this urgent meeting had been held for no other reason than to divide the spoils of their treachery.

Stalin had only just died, and his body had not yet been placed in the hall where the final homage was to be paid. The program for the organization of paying homage and the funeral ceremony were still not worked out. The Soviet people were weeping over their great loss while the top Soviet leadership found the time to share their portfolios. Major changes were made in all the top organizations of the Party and the state that day. The Presidium and the Bureau of the

Presidium of the Central Committee of the Party were merged into a single organization. New secretaries of the Central Committee of the Party were elected, a number of ministries were amalgamated or united, and changes were made in the Presidium of the Supreme Soviets.

Caleb paused and looked up. Forde wasn't sure if Caleb was paraphrasing or reciting the end of Hoxha's memo from memory.

Disturbing questions arose automatically. How were all these major changes made so suddenly in one day—and not just any ordinary day but on the first day of mourning? Logic compels us to believe that everything had been prepared in advance. These changes had been worked out long before. It is never possible to make such extremely important decisions in a few hours, even on a completely normal day. However, if at the start these were only doubts that shocked and surprised us, later developments and the occurrences and facts we were to learn subsequently made us even more convinced that hidden hands had prepared the plot long before and then waited for the opportunity.

Forde still had his doubts. "So why Hoxha? Why would he say anything about this to the Agency?"

Caleb wondered if Forde was baiting him or just knew nothing about the dynamics in the Soviet Bloc. "Hoxha was an anti-revisionist," Caleb told Forde. "He was loyal to Stalin and hated Khrushchev for the changes to the pure brand of communism Stalin had practiced. When Khrushchev cozied up to Tito, Hoxha's archenemy in 1960, that was the last straw for Hoxha. He became a Maoist."

"Okay, Dr. Young. Your facts do add up to some smoke, but whether there is some fire behind it or it is just a screen because Hoxha was angry with Khrushchev for his policies will have to be sorted out by historians."

Caleb frowned and seemed annoyed. "Just remember, you asked and I reached my conclusion based on the facts before me."

Forde was perturbed. "We have been here four months spinning our wheels. We need to move on to Ike and then Kennedy. While you do that, I still want to know about who frightens you so much that when we start to peel the onion back, you clam up."

Caleb remained implacable. *Forde, if you only knew the consequences for you and your family. . . .* "I will be moving on to Eisenhower's massive retaliation policy as well as the development and implementation of the U-2. You will learn who controls the SIOP-62 and SIOP–63 plans as well as the NSTL—the National Strategic Target List—within the military that will annihilate 350 million communists within 12 hours. Will that make you more comfortable . . . or less?"

Forde looked distressed. "Go on with your narrative . . . for now."

Caleb didn't care how Forde felt and kept going. "The Army promoted Nikita Khrushchev to First Secretary of the Communist Party of the Soviet Union but allowed Georgy Malenkov to succeed Stalin as Premier. This was an important development for the United States because General Eisenhower and Soviet General Zhukov had strong social ties dating back to the end of World War II. A lot of people, including the good folks at *Time* magazine, thought Malenkov would rise to the top, but the CIA—the Agency—predicted the eventual winner all along.

"Several years later, the Director of Central Intelligence, the DCI as we call him, confirmed that Khrushchev and Zhukov had canceled Stalin's Operation Mighty Handful. Khrushchev admitted publicly that this Jewish pogrom was merely intended to be an elaborate hoax."

∽

May 1, 1953 – 0700 Hours
The Kremlin Senate Building
Stalin's Small Office

"I did him in! I saved all of you!" Soviet Marshal Lavrentiy Beria clenched his fists in triumph.

Vyacheslav Molotov, Russia's foreign minister, looked at Beria with disgust. "You'd better damn well shut your mouth before you get all of us tortured and executed. The MVD investigators are already asking Bulganin, Khrushchev, Malenkov, and me about Stalin's death. If we say the word, you will disappear like spit on a hot skillet. Never mention *the incident* again, or I will have you shot."

2

April 1964
Office of William Forde, Esq., Chief of
the Criminal Division and CIA Liaison
950 Pennsylvania Avenue, Suite 710
Washington, DC

Forde scrutinized Caleb with his head tilted. "Didn't go so well for Beria, did it?"

Caleb shook his head. "With General Zhukov's able and ruthless assistance, Khrushchev prevailed. Beria was arrested, tried for treason, and executed two days before Christmas in 1953. He was 54 years old. Interestingly, after he was dead and could not defend himself against slander, there were widespread rumors about his affinity for rape and sexual predation."

"I knew he was a killer," Forde added. "Any thoughts on the validity of the other charges?"

"No doubt they were true," Caleb said. "Too many reports, too many details. Even Stalin, who introduced Beria to President Truman as his Himmler, knew how ruthless and deadly he was. By comparison, Khrushchev was a saint."

There was no response from Forde. Caleb took it as assent for him to continue. But first, Forde had to satisfy his curiosity.

"What was going on in the US intelligence community during the last few months of Stalin's life?" Forde asked. "And how did everyone miss Operation Mighty Handful? It would have been a major geopolitical and military catastrophe for the Western powers."

"We didn't miss it," Caleb claimed. "I'll get to it in due time, but let's cover the surprising relatively peaceful transition of power in a country where Stalin was a dictator."

"Okay, go on then."

"Remember, this was only the second time in the history of the world that an atomic power had a leadership vacancy. The Western powers waited with some trepidation as the Soviet Union named five men one by one to the new office of Secretariat of the Communist Party.[1] Most assumed that Georgy Malenkov, who was named Soviet Premier and leader of the Communist Party on March 6, 1953, would orchestrate a smooth transition. But he made the mistake of underestimating Khrushchev who had been a Party member since 1918 and had deep political ties.

"By September 1953, old Nikita had organized a coalition of Soviet politicians to force Malenkov to relinquish his position as First Secretary.[2] It was an important post since it controlled the Party apparatus. Khrushchev would later assume full power and name Bulganin, a trusted friend and co-conspirator, as Premier. Malenkov was relegated to inconsequential roles. He had a brilliant scientific mind but no feel for the art of politics. And at the same time, there was a transition in the United States."

Caleb took a drink of water while he let the Stalin-to-Khrushchev transition sink in. Forde wasn't surprised at what he heard, but he was visibly anxious to hear much more.

"Before Stalin died," Caleb continued, "he would often have discussions with other members of the Politburo about who the next leader of the United States would be. It was an election year in 1952, and after the New Hampshire primary, it was clear that Truman would not be reelected. But Truman didn't want the next president to be blindsided like he had been. Remember, on Truman's thirteenth day in office, Secretary of War Henry Stinson dropped the bomb about the bomb."

Caleb chuckled at his own little joke. Forde grimaced.

The man has no sense of humor, Caleb thought.

"Anyway," Caleb went on, "in August 1952, Truman instructed the DCI, General Bedell Smith, and other members of his administration handling matters of national security to start briefings for Senator Adlai Stevenson, the Democratic nominee, and General Dwight Eisenhower, the Republican nominee. For five months, I met with the two nominees numerous times. But you need to understand where our oral and written briefings of Truman stood in the last half of 1952."

"You do love your rabbit trails, don't you, Dr. Young?"

"I take things seriatim," Caleb said. "Do you want a thorough picture or not?"

"Proceed," Forde said. "But let's not forget that Christmas is coming this year."

"I anticipate we will be finished with this section in plenty of time."

Caleb thought Forde mumbled something about "from your lips to God's ears," but he let it pass.

"As you know," Caleb went on, "in January 1951, the daily and weekly summaries were replaced by the current intelligence bulletin and the intelligence weekly review when the CIA formed the Office of Current Intelligence, aka the OCI. Melvin Hendrickson, head of the military branch in OCI's Indications Staff, was part of our briefing team.[3] The only other periodic intelligence document produced by the Agency at that time was the Situation Summary, which primarily dealt with signal intercepts from Korea.

"DCI Smith, CIA officer Meredith Davidson, Melvin Hendrickson, and I normally met every Friday with Truman who was ever mindful of the situation he'd encountered after Roosevelt died. With every good intention, he sent telegrams to Stevenson and Eisenhower, inviting them to a top-level meeting on August 19, 1952, and offered to share with them his weekly briefings. Eisenhower declined the invitation, which by itself would have been enough to upset Truman. But Eisenhower's reply—"

Caleb stopped for a moment to pick up one of the many binders on the table and refer to his notes. He wanted to be nothing less than accurate.

"But Eisenhower's reply, this man destined to be the next president, was this:

As you know, the problems which you suggest for discussion are those with which I have lived for many years. . . . With respect to the weekly reports from the Central Intelligence Agency that you kindly offered to send me, I will welcome these reports. In line with my view, however, that the American people are entitled to all the facts in the international situation, save only in those cases where the security of the United States is involved, I would want it understood that the possession of these reports will in no other way limit my freedom to discuss or analyze foreign programs as my judgment dictates.

"Truman irritated Eisenhower further by releasing the text of Eisenhower's telegram to the press. On August 16, 1952, he sent Eisenhower this handwritten note:

Dear Ike:

I am sorry if I caused you embarrassment. What I've always had in mind was and is a continuing foreign policy. You know that it is a fact, because you had a part in outlining it.

Partisan politics should stop at the boundaries of the United States. I am extremely sorry that you have allowed a bunch of screwballs to come between us. You have made a bad mistake and I'm hoping it won't injure this great Republic. There has never been one like it and I want to see it continue regardless of the man who occupies the most important position in the history of the world.

May God guide you and give you light.

From a man who has always been your friend and who always wanted to be!

Sincerely,
Harry Truman.[4]

"To Eisenhower's credit, he decided to dial down the rhetoric. After he vented his frustration to General Bedell Smith, he consented to periodic CIA briefings from Davidson, Hendrickson, and me to stay current on Korea and the Soviets."

"Touchy people, these politicians," Forde quipped.

Caleb nodded and continued. "Over the next eight years, I realized my initial impressions of Eisenhower were shortsighted despite his refusal to come to the White House for coffee just prior to the traditional ride to the inauguration. His comment about not being sure he could sit beside 'that man' during the ride was uncalled for, even if Truman's campaign speeches on behalf of Adlai Stevenson had been upsetting."

Forde looked like he was about to smirk but caught himself and looked down. Caleb went on.

"You can trace the origin of the ill feelings between the two men to a statement Truman made while campaigning for Adlai Stevenson earlier in the year. Truman called Eisenhower a coward for failing to condemn Senator Joseph McCarthy's attack on General George Marshall, who had been Eisenhower's superior as Chairman of the Joint Chiefs of Staff. During World War II, President Roosevelt had sent Eisenhower to Europe to assume field command of the Allied effort because he viewed Marshall's plan for an Anglo-American invasion of France in 1943 as too ambitious. He felt Marshall's main strength was in organizational skills as opposed to field command."

Caleb was getting more animated talking about the war. He barely took a breath and carried on. "Churchill would belatedly laud the decision because he knew it would take someone of Eisenhower's caliber to get along with General Bernard Montgomery. Eisenhower understood Marshall's great disappointment. Moving ahead, Eisenhower was set to deliver a speech denouncing Senator Joseph R. McCarthy's characterization of General Marshall as being 'part of a communist conspiracy' when both Wisconsin Governor Walter Kohler Jr. and Senator McCarthy indicated they would withdraw their support for Eisenhower, which would have jeopardized Eisenhower's chances in Wisconsin.

"Regretfully, Eisenhower caved in and in the process deserted the man who would win the 1953 Nobel Peace Prize—George C. Marshall. In so doing, Eisenhower tacitly embraced McCarthy who was claiming that the communists had infiltrated the nation's schools, unions, news media, and government. It was a low point in Eisenhower's otherwise distinguished military and political career."

Forde looked a little lost. Caleb realized that Forde didn't know any of the machinations he had just described. Like most other Americans, Forde worshiped at the altar of the World War II commander and hero and preferred not to see the warts, blemishes, and humanness.

∽

August 30, 1952 – 0745 Hours
Undisclosed Location
Washington, DC

Although Eisenhower had specifically requested Young's presence, he expressed some reservations about the scientist to General Smith. It was not so much about Caleb's ability to edit and prepare final drafts of national intelligence estimates or his scientific credentials as it was about his personal life. It was hard for Eisenhower to imagine a man with no personal life outside the Agency or scientific committees. Eisenhower contacted all three former CIA Directors—Rear Admiral Souers, General Vandenberg, and Rear Admiral Hillenkoetter. He'd met all of them during his military service. They all confirmed Bedell's assessment of Young's vanilla lifestyle.

At the culmination of his inquiry, Eisenhower remarked, "Damn, Beedle." Ike called him Beedle. "I don't know if I can trust a man with no interest in power, women, or money. Is he on Hoover's team?"

Bedell laughed and said, "No interest there either, General. He has been carefully watched by our own Internal Affairs and the FBI's domestic surveillance team for over six years, and we have interviewed the scientists who worked with him on the Manhattan Project. Nothing but math and science . . . and basketball on occasion."

Eisenhower wanted more, so Smith continued.

"If you go back and attempt to trace his lineage, you won't get much about him prior to 1930 and even less about his parents. They were both physicists at the University of California, Berkeley. Former DCI Souers has some handwritten notes about Dr. Young's mother being in the same college class as Lise Meitner, who was credited along with Otto Hahn for splitting the first atom in a lab in Munich in 1939. But if she was, we can't trace either of the other two females in her class to the United States. Souers admitted that the Agency deleted all the information the Office of Strategic Services had gathered on Dr. Young either because it was redundant or could not be verified."

"Well," Eisenhower said, "if he's half as good as you say, nothing else matters. Still kind of an oddball, but most of the great physicists are half a bubble off plumb and don't know it."

3

April 1964
Office of William Forde, Esq., Chief of
the Criminal Division and CIA Liaison
950 Pennsylvania Avenue, Suite 710
Washington, DC

"I hadn't met Eisenhower," Caleb went on. "General Smith told me about the briefing and how he'd given Ike copies of my FBI and CIA dossiers. I knew Eisenhower loved projects designed to connect military planning with research and development from educational foundations and institutions. So I figured my involvement with the Air Defense Study of the RAND Committee and my Beacon Hill report called 'Problems of Air Force Intelligence and Reconnaissance' interested the presidential candidate.[5]

"The Agency's briefing material followed a set format. There were twenty or so short items summarized in a few paragraphs. They dealt with specific countries in order of significance. They always started with the Soviet, Chinese, Korean, and Iranian situations. There followed a longer article on what we thought was the most significant development. The written material also contained a conclusions section, which was a summary of the most recent national intelligence estimates. At the time of the briefing, Hendrickson was head of the military branch in OCI's Indications Staff. He had several years of military experience. His post had been the assistant military attaché in Oslo."[6]

"Let's move this along, Doctor," Forde said. "I don't need to know what brand of cologne everyone wore."

15

"A little early in the day to be so fussy," Caleb said. "Does someone need a nap?"

Forde got the point and scowled. He pointed to the material in front of Caleb, who nodded.

"It was August 30, 1952. We were waiting in the library at Eisenhower's residence at Columbia University in Manhattan, New York City. Eisenhower entered at exactly 0745 hours, the time we had agreed to meet. Military to the core. For reasons I will never understand, we stood. I mean, really, the man had been the Supreme Commander of NATO, but he was technically a civilian."

"War hero, savior of the free world, candidate for President. That not enough for you?" Forde asked. "Please tell me you gave him the courtesy."

"I did. But social conventions are such a waste of time."

"Would you have stood for the newly coronated Queen of England? Or the pope?"

"Certainly, but they were leaders of sovereign nations. Ike was just someone running for President."

Forde pinched the bridge of his nose like a man with a migraine but said nothing.

"Hendrickson spent twenty minutes going over the reports," Caleb explained. "Once Eisenhower confirmed the static nature of the deployment of the Soviet Bloc's forces, he started commenting on the situation in Iran where the Soviets had not removed their troops as agreed. He went over France's growing difficulties in North Africa and Japan's balance of trade with China. Regarding the latter, he stated, 'Since trade is one of our most powerful weapons, it seems to me that we should employ it to its maximum. Where are the Japanese going to get their materials if they can't get them from China?' He was also certain the French were going to have 'another Indochina' on their hands in Africa if they didn't get their house in order."[7]

"The man understood geopolitics," Forde said.

"True," Caleb said. "Anyway, after the briefing, Eisenhower asked me to stay. He noticed I had not spoken during the briefing, and he wanted my opinion vis-à-vis US air defenses and aircraft reconnaissance. As I suspected, he'd read my reports."

"I'm sure you shared," Forde said.

"Your sarcasm aside," Caleb said, "when asked my opinion, I will give it—straightforward and unvarnished."

"No holds barred, I assume."

"Yes."

"Well, what do you think of my tie?" Forde asked.

"I was wondering which of your children gave it to you. That would be the only explanation for wearing something so hideous."

"Mother-in-law."

"And people wonder why I never married."

"Want to know what I think of your suit?" Forde asked.

"Your sartorial opinion makes no difference to me and is not germane to our discussion."

Forde looked disappointed. "Go ahead."

"I told Ike that my position differed from the Agency's in regard to the Soviet's intentions in Western Europe and was not widely shared by others except for the Deputy Director, Allen Dulles. I could tell by Eisenhower's facial expression that he was upset. Eisenhower said to me, 'Dr. Young, how in hell are the differences of opinion between you and the Deputy Director not in this briefing? Spill it! Now!'

"I turned to Eisenhower and said, 'Sir, I don't think we can rely on Agent Hendrickson's conclusions. He stated, and I quote, "The Soviet forces have maintained a static position from the date of Eisenhower's resignation as the Supreme Allied Commander in Europe for NATO forces." There is just too much guesswork going into his estimations. There is insufficient data within the class of indicators utilized. Even with more information, it's not sufficient to reach any conclusions. While our reports have some validity, they should not be taken as anything other than mere suggestions. They are not holy writ. I don't want to go into great detail concerning why I believe those indicators are suspect because my opinion within the Agency is in the minority.'

"Then Eisenhower leaned in and asked me, 'Dr. Young, what are you suggesting we use in lieu of these imperfect indicators?' I said to him, 'General, I think you already know the answer because you have read and reviewed my reports. We need a high-altitude reconnaissance plane with a range of over 3,000 miles. It must be capable of operating at an altitude above 65,000 feet. We already have or will very soon have cameras with high enough resolution to visualize any objects of interest from over 75,000 feet.'

"Eisenhower said to me, 'Thank you for your candor.' And that's how I left it. I said one last thing to Eisenhower. 'It probably didn't hurt that I admitted a total lack of knowledge on the trade issue between Japan and China, or what France should or shouldn't do in North Africa.'"

"That must have pinched a little," Forde said.

"Not at all," Caleb responded. "I know when I am out of my depth. I have very good ball handling skills—even at my age. But I am not a point guard. I know when to pass."

Forde sniffed.

"Eisenhower received three more pre-election briefings. I attended them all. In preparation, I reviewed my position on the increasing likelihood of Soviet aggression with a CIA panel consisting of Deputy Director of Intelligence Robert Amory, nuclear specialist Dr. Herbert Miller, and Dr. Herbert Scoville Jr., Assistant Director for Scientific Intelligence. Dulles and I remained in the minority. The others believed that what Stalin wanted was to be certain that a preemptive strike would emasculate our industrial base. The Director and I suspected Stalin was focused on Italy and France. Based on Rand 227, I believed the Russians could damage but not destroy our industrial base. The briefings continued without a consensus."

Caleb took a well-needed pause to drink some water, with no ice. "On September 25th, 1952, Hendrickson and I boarded Eisenhower's campaign train in Silver Spring, Maryland,

and briefed him during the short trip to Baltimore.[8] As usual, Eisenhower studied the written material for about twenty minutes and then made some general comments about Korea and Iran. He said if he got the job, he would be taking action to force the Russians completely out of Iran and push the Chinese to the bargaining table in Korea.

"The third pre-election briefing took place in Denver, Colorado, on October 11, 1952, at the Eisenhowers' suite in the Brown Palace Hotel that came to be known as the Western White House. It was a Saturday morning, and Eisenhower seemed unusually jovial. After the briefing, he invited Hendrickson and me to a rodeo in Denver that weekend. We all rode together in a stagecoach—General and Mrs. Eisenhower inside and Hendrickson and I on top as shotgun with the driver. I was beginning to think that Eisenhower was just a regular fellow, someone who processed information and then arrived at a decision without any preconceived notions and based solely on the acuity of his intelligence. Still, he had the capacity to cut you off at the knees if he felt the need to do so. I was right."

"What happened?' Forde asked.

"All in good time," Caleb said. "The fourth pre-election briefing took place two weeks later on October 25, 1952. Hendrickson and I boarded Eisenhower's campaign train in the early morning hours at Harmon Station, New York, and briefed Eisenhower on the way to Grand Central Station in New York City.[9] I could tell during the briefing process that I was gaining Eisenhower's trust—a crucial factor over the next six months. I discussed the meetings I'd held with Colonel Richard Leghorn and the English Electric Canberra Company. The PR3 Canberra aircraft, as modified by Leghorn's design, could attain 65,000 feet and was the best we could hope for as a short-term solution."

Almost chuckling, Caleb added, "Eisenhower surprised me. He knew all about the Canberra. He knew about the Rolls-Royce Avon 109 engines. He stressed that we could not have a plane shot down over Russia or any of its satellite states. When he was Supreme Allied Commander Europe—or SACEUR as we called it—the Canberra could not rise above 50,000 feet. He wanted to talk more but he stressed the importance of winning the election and said he needed to focus on the situation in Korea.

"When I left that meeting, I had a newfound respect for Eisenhower's ability to grasp the importance of first-rate airborne reconnaissance. I didn't meet with Eisenhower again until after he was elected on Tuesday, November 4th."

4

November 21, 1952 – 1000 Hours
Train Station
Baltimore, Maryland

President-elect Dwight David Eisenhower lit up when he saw Meredith Davidson. They'd met several times at the Pentagon for briefings just after the war. Davidson made a joke about fighting in "the real war in the Pacific." Ike laughed.

Since Eisenhower seemed in a good mood, DCI Smith joked about Davidson's briefing the opposition, Adlai Stevenson, in Springfield, Illinois. Eisenhower turned his icy blue stare toward Smith. "I will hear nothing derogatory about Mr. Stevenson," he said. "The man ran a clean campaign and demonstrated a mastery of foreign affairs."

The atmosphere in the train station sobered a little, a mood that stretched into the briefing. This one, after all, counted—Ike was the President-elect, having won the election by a landslide just 17 days earlier. He was beginning to realize the daunting nature of the job he was about to begin. He would be facing daily questions of serious import.

At one point during a discussion about the Korean situation, Eisenhower said, "I never did know why we let the Chinese call themselves volunteers."

DCI Smith deadpanned. "We didn't have to bomb Peking. That's why we acquiesced."[10]

The exchange took place near the end of a three-and-a-half-hour briefing during which Eisenhower loosened up quite a bit. He took the comment in stride and resumed his upbeat demeanor. At one point, his wife, Mamie Eisenhower, who took part in two of the briefings, expressed an opinion slightly contrary to the President's. Smith couldn't resist blurting out in jest, "That is the first time I've seen an order of a five-star general and Commander in Chief overruled!"

Overall, the give-and-take between Eisenhower and Smith was fluid even though Eisenhower ultimately turned down Smith's request to be named chairman of the Joint Chiefs of Staff.[11] Instead, he was appointed deputy director under John Foster Dulles in the State Department. General Smith was extremely disappointed and quit the State Department after about a year and a half.

∽

November 28, 1952
Commodore Hotel
New York City

Seven days after the train station meeting, Eisenhower requested a secret briefing on Korea. Smith's detail and Caleb Young met him at the Commodore Hotel in New York. They arrived at 1345 hours. Army security personnel took them in through the front door of a drug store about a block from the Commodore. They scurried out the back, through the alley, into the hotel, and up the service elevator to Eisenhower's offices. When they sat down in the waiting room, they saw William Donovan among those leaving the President-elect's office. DCI Smith remarked that he was unsure of Donovan's status but knew Eisenhower had depended on him for intelligence during the war. Donovan had been linked to some questionable activities; it was a little disconcerting to know he still had Eisenhower's ear.

Because of the secrecy, a security escort for the trip to the Commodore was out of the question. Sheffield, Director of Security at the Agency, convinced Meredith Davidson, who was weapons qualified, to arm himself for the trip. That was a bad move. Shortly after the briefing commenced, the Secret Service saw Davidson's weapon protruding from his shoulder harness and took him to the ground. Caleb wasn't used to such excitement. When the issue was resolved, DCI Smith was asked about his intelligence assessment.

"Mr. President," Smith began, "the Soviets could be very close to engaging us on the battlefield in a more direct fashion. As you know, their pilots are currently flying MiG-15s and ground support aircraft, and supplying North Korea with most of their arms. Any way you can bring this conflict to a conclusion should be considered, including the use of nuclear weapons. I sense the commanders in the field feel we are fighting for a stalemate—not great for morale. All the other information you requested is laid out in our report. It's been abbreviated to approximately five pages."

Eisenhower thanked Smith for his prompt assessment and lamented the fact that Smith would be resigning as DCI with an effective date of February 9, 1953. Smith said he was more than capable of working with John Foster Dulles, the new Secretary of State. Later that day, the men ran into Dulles in the lobby of the Waldorf Astoria Hotel. Dulles let them know that he knew about the meeting earlier that day and asked what they had told Ike.[12]

"That's between him and me," DCI Smith said.

Not the best way for a neophyte diplomat to begin a career at the State Department.

∽

January 24, 1953
Trieste, Italy

Milovan Djilas, the Deputy Prime Minister of Yugoslavia, had collaborated with Yugoslav politician Edvard Kardelj during the tripartite military delegation talks held November 16–20, 1952. The primary question had been what level of military cooperation Yugoslavia could expect from the West if Stalin chose to make Yugoslavia another Korea. From July to December 1952, the United States sent $70 million in financial aid to Yugoslavia.

The tripartite delegation was headed on one side by US General Thomas T. Handy and on the other by Yugoslavia's Chief of the General Staff, General Peko Dapčević. The Yugoslavian government sought assurances from the tripartite military delegation that there would be an agreement to defend Yugoslavia against Soviet satellite aggression. Even though the tripartite military commission was not willing to make such a pledge, Yugoslavia's Premier Tito sought a closer alliance with NATO allies, Greece, and Turkey. He was trying to get his foot in the door. He wanted NATO's involvement in case of a Soviet-inspired attack.

Djilas set up a meeting with US agent Pavlo Rheghetti in northeast Italy to provide some limited information about Operation Mighty Handful. The exchange between the two was revealing.

Djilas got right to the point. "The Soviet GRU and NKVD have been shipping heavy armaments to the Communist Parties in Italy and France. We do not know the purpose of the shipments but believe them to be related to attacks on NATO air bases in conjunction with a proposed major offensive action. It's just the tip of the iceberg. We keep a close watch on the neighboring states of Bulgaria and Romania as well as Albania. There has been a marked increase of activity not only with troop movements but also with more air power being placed at strategic locations in these countries. I know your country has the ability to monitor electronic traffic, including communication intercepts. Your intelligence agency should pay close attention to the keywords 'Mighty Handful.' Much more than that I can't tell you other than to be vigilant in the near future."

Rheghetti's response was immediate. "What makes you think the attack is imminent? Aren't these just normal Soviet maneuvers in response to NATO military exercises?"

"The Soviets are shipping heavy ordinance into locations along their satellites' borders. It can be moved quickly into striking range of NATO air bases. The troop movements we see are mechanized reserve units. They are replacing Soviet frontline troops that are stationed less than 50 miles from the front with satellite reserves. That is what they would do to attack the West in an offensive action because of the high initial attrition rate. Even though the airways are full of chatter about the regular troops rotating out, I emphasize that *they are not returning home.* NATO is going to be attacked soon."

"Is that it?" Rheghetti asked.

"Yes. Just remember where this information came from. We have informal agreements with Greece and Turkey for the defense of our region. I know Eisenhower and Secretary Dulles are hardcore anti-communists. Don't let a form of government paint us all with the same brush. Remember, we are not a bellicose, hegemonic monster seeking to overthrow democratically elected officials. We want what you want— peace and prosperity. Yugoslav Marshal Tito remembers where the millions in aid came from."

∾

January 26, 1953 – 0800 Hours
Office of Deputy Director of Intelligence
Robert Amory Jr.
CIA Headquarters
Langley, Virginia

The frost between DCI Smith and Eisenhower was palpable after their meeting on December 19, 1952. Smith's last briefing was on January 14, 1953, in New York City. The DCI was joined by John Foster Dulles and other soon-to-be cabinet members for an in-depth foreign policy conference. President-elect Eisenhower wanted weekly briefings with the National Security Council (NSC) every Wednesday or Thursday at 0900 hours.[13] James Lay Jr., Executive Secretary of the NSC, would work with the new President and cabinet members to select the topics. The conversation in Trieste, Italy, topped the list.

Now, on January 26, 1953, they met at Langley, the CIA's headquarters. Eisenhower, DCI Smith, James Lay, and CIA Deputy Director Robert Amory Jr. were there. Since Smith was nursing a bruised ego, Amory took the lead. Lay had already been agitated "in extremis" with Amory.

"Robert," Lay began, "the President wants everything you have on this Trieste matter. We are adding the Chief of Staff and the civilian secretaries of all three branches of the military on the 29th. General LeMay will attend. So will General Matthew Ridgeway as SACEUR from NATO. The Agency will send Davidson, Hendricks, and Caleb Young as well. What is your take on this intelligence?"

"The situation may require the President to raise our readiness alert status," Amory said.

"Won't that tip off the Soviets?" Lay asked.

"There could be worse things than their calling off the party because we ruined the surprise," Amory responded.

"Good point," Lay agreed. "Anyway, send everything you have, no matter how insignificant. Ike does like details, you know."

When the meeting adjourned, Amory called Caleb into his office. "Caleb, I saw your notes on this Mighty Handful business. Thoughts?"

"Robert, this isn't anything with which to trifle. It has the makings of another Pearl Harbor."

Robert Amory fiddled with a letter opener—a replica of an M1 bayonet. He thought about all the men who'd had to use one and what another global conflict would mean.

"Dr. Young," Amory said without looking up. "You are taking the lead on the briefing on the 29th. Be aggressive. You've covered everything in your multiple reports and studies. We're covering our assets here. If we get hit, it won't be because we didn't sound the alarm."

Caleb's expression didn't change. He took a moment to clean his glasses with a handkerchief.

Amory pointed. "Monogrammed. Nice touch."

"Belonged to my mother," Caleb said. "The only personal item of hers I have."

Amory opened his mouth, but Caleb didn't let him ask the question. "I don't talk about my parents. Besides, it's not germane to our discussion."

What son doesn't want to talk about his mother? Amory thought.

Caleb continued. "You sure I'm the one? I get a little in the weeds sometimes. The President likes short, concise answers in NSC meetings."

Amory shook his head. "Not this time. Ike smells a rat, and he wants to root it out. He'll want details. I'll get you a longer leash. You go until someone cuts you off."

5

January 29, 1953 – 0800 Hours
Oval Office, White House
Washington, DC

Eisenhower paced behind the desk, his golf spikes clattering on the hardwood floor. He muttered to himself, "I ordered almost 4,500 boys to their deaths on D-Day. I thought that was bad. Now I'm debating nuclear options destined to kill millions based on the speculations of some egghead."

He stared at the twenty-page memo on his desk—Dr. Caleb Young's assessment. While accurate to the nth degree, intelligence-wise the conclusions were guesswork at best.

Even the smartest guy in the room makes mistakes, Eisenhower said only to himself.

He looked at his shoes and huffed. "Mamie's going to kill me. I am chewing up the very floors Lincoln walked on. Of course, they were already seventy years old when Lincoln was worrying about Gettysburg."

The President sat down, reached under his desk, and pulled out his dress shoes. He pushed a button in the knee well. The door opened in less than five seconds. Howell Crim, Chief Usher of the White House, nodded.

"Mr. President, how is the putting stroke?"

"Shakier than a trollop's morals," Eisenhower said. "But it might have been the cold. Tell the fellas on the grounds crew how much I appreciate their sweeping off the snow so I could practice a little. Helps take my mind off things for a while."

"Certainly, sir."

Eisenhower held up his spikes. "Would you have Harold brush these up?"

"Yes, sir."

"And Howell—"

The veteran usher held up a palm. "I know, sir. When Mrs. Eisenhower asks, I haven't seen a thing."

"Good man," Eisenhower said. "No wonder you've been here almost twenty years."

The President knew all too well what might be over the horizon. He had officially been President of the United States for just nine days, and he was already wondering if the country was ready to go to war over the loss of limited territory in Europe. What type of war was NATO willing to conduct? A protracted conventional war was almost certainly out of the question. He quickly ran the most updated report of NATO and Eastern Bloc forces through his head. NATO had sixteen to eighteen available viable divisions for the defense of all Western Europe. The Soviet Bloc had nearly 200. Within ninety days of the initiation of hostilities, the Soviet Bloc could expand its forces to 400 divisions.

The United States had a total of twenty active divisions spread around the globe, eight of which were in Korea. The Soviets had never torn down their industrial warmaking machine at the end of World War II. They chose to continue cranking out tanks and combat planes while the United States made tractors. Eisenhower could envision the sea of 6,100 hammer-and-sickle-stamped tanks washing over the landscape with air support from more than 7,000 jets and 14,000 propeller-driven combat planes. The Soviet navy continued its aggressive expansion and now featured more long-range subs and deep-water missile battle cruisers.

The CIA had identified the three bases from which the Soviets might launch an attack on the United States—the Chukotski Peninsula in northeast Siberia, the Kola Peninsula in northwestern USSR, and Soviet-controlled territory along the Baltic and East Germany. These areas afforded the shortest route to the continental United States. With one in-flight refueling, the bombers could reach any target in America. The Chukotski Peninsula base was nearest to the United States. The standard Tu-4 with no in-flight refueling could not reach the United States.[14]

"Excuse me, Mr. President," Howell said.

Eisenhower looked up.

"Mr. President, the gentlemen from the CIA are here."

The group trundled in.

"Gentlemen," Eisenhower said, "I've read Dr. Young's report. I'm more than a little bit disturbed about why our surveillance planes can't confirm what's happening on the ground."

Everyone's head turned to Caleb Young.

"Mr. President," Caleb responded, "we only received the information forty-eight hours ago. We continue to check our sources."

"So your gut tells you Stalin is going to launch a major offensive on the Western Front in an attempt to take over a large portion of Western Europe—maybe even all of West Germany—and this is going to happen sometime in the next thirty days?"

"We can't rule that out, Mr. President."

Eisenhower shook his head. "Dr. Young, you're asking me to invade Normandy after someone read the tea leaves? I need more. You admit the reports from our so-called agents might be false."

"Mr. President, I know you haven't had time to go over the entire twenty-page report with your customary detail," Caleb responded, "but I am very confident that what is happening in the Soviet Union and in particular the Eastern Bloc constitutes more than military exercises."

Eisenhower could have been watching the trees blowing in the wind. His expression never changed. Caleb didn't hesitate. "We have been following the movements of the Baltic and Black Sea fleets and in particular the positioning of their submarines in the Mediterranean Sea. We believe there are more than sixty

Soviet submarines with advanced classifications operating in the Mediterranean at this time. Lately, the Soviet Air Force has been very aggressive in intercepting and shooting down our reconnaissance planes. Consequently, we haven't been able to verify the scarce data and intel we have received from our on-the-ground assets concerning the location and number of heavy bombers."

Everyone stood when Eisenhower did.

"Okay," Eisenhower said. "Let's head on over to the Cabinet Room. Dr. Young, many people are waiting for us there, and I want a full rundown on our strategic vulnerability. Everyone needs to understand the danger we face from a Soviet first strike. Everyone in this administration needs to know where the Soviet bombers are staged and the areas those bombers can reach in the United States. I want the big picture first. After the meeting, we'll take the next week to analyze the thirty-day attack scenario."

⤫

January 29, 1953 – 0900 Hours
Cabinet Room – West Wing
National Security Council Meeting
The White House, Washington, DC

In attendance:
    President Dwight D. Eisenhower, presiding
    Vice President Richard M. Nixon
    Charles E. Wilson, Secretary of Defense
    John Foster Dulles, Secretary of State
    Arthur Fleming, Secretary of Health, Education, and Welfare
    General Omar N. Bradley, Chairman, Joint Chiefs of Staff
    Admiral William M. Fechteler, Navy Chief of Staff
    General Hoyt S. Vandenberg, Air Force Chief of Staff
    General J. Lawton Collins, Army Chief of Staff

Harold E. Talbott, Secretary of the Air Force
Robert B. Anderson, Secretary of the Navy
Robert T. Stevens, Secretary of the Army
General Matthew B. Ridgeway, Supreme Allied
    Commander Europe
General Curtis E. LeMay, Commander, Strategic Air Command
Representatives of the Central Intelligence Agency (names
    redacted)

President Eisenhower called the meeting to order. "I don't have to tell anyone in this room about the seriousness of the special intelligence estimate we received from the CIA just a few days ago. Dr. Caleb Young, who has been the Chief Science Officer at the CIA since its inception in 1947, has prepared final drafts of the documents in front of you. Over the years, he has been quite prescient. He believes there is a credible threat of a Soviet attack. You received his twenty-page summary yesterday. I trust you all digested it before you read the sports pages."

There was some uneasy laughter, but every head nodded.

"He will go over the written material and then give an oral presentation, after which he will take questions. Dr. Young."

As Caleb approached the wall-sized map he had prepared for this briefing, it occurred to him how offended some of the attendees might be. His summary of Project Vista excoriated the Air Force for its view regarding its primary functions—strategic bombing and interdiction of incoming Soviet long-range bombers. Their refusal to adopt Robert Oppenheimer's proposal to devote even a minimal amount of their budget and assets to tactical delivery of smaller nuclear ordnance in support of ground troops left a gaping hole in the options available to the President if the Soviets chose to start a limited war anywhere along the East-West divide in Western Europe. Eisenhower would have to choose between an all-or-none response when it really didn't have to be that way.

Dr. Young's presentation was also an affront to the Army. He advised the Army to concentrate reinforcements in northern rather than southern and central Germany. He thought the Soviets would launch an attack more suited to the terrain found in the northern plains than the mountainous and hilly terrain. He had reviewed other aspects, but his presentation dealt primarily with the potential for nuclear bombing of cities in the continental United States (CONUS).

While most of the top military advisors refused to believe the Soviets would launch hundreds of planes on one-way trips to the United States, President Eisenhower (without publicly stating such) secretly feared that the danger of a second Pearl Harbor was real. Eisenhower was even more convinced after Dr. Young met with him.

Caleb Young nodded to President Eisenhower. "Thank you, Mr. President. Gentlemen, our best estimate is that the Soviets have 175 active divisions fully manned, fully armed, and combat-ready. We estimate about half a million soldiers are forward deployed in Eastern Europe. More than 75 percent of these can be found in the German Democratic Republic. The Soviets have scattered the others throughout potential hotspots determined by Stalin."

He continued to rattle off statistics from memory . . .

Seventy-five divisions in Eastern Bloc satellite states . . .

Nine airborne divisions . . .

100,000 troops . . .

A total of 400 divisions . . .

Five and a half million men at arms.

The more he talked, the less anyone moved. They were nocturnal wildlife frozen in the intense brightness of a hunting lamp—knowing danger was near but unable to move.

Caleb went on without noticing them. "The Russians have more than 1,000 Tu-4 heavy bombers, all of which are capable of reaching targets in the CONUS either on one-way Jimmy Dolittle–type missions or on round-trip operations if complemented by inbound, in-flight refueling and/or structural modifications.

"In addition, the Soviets have more than 8,000 MiG-15s and more than 1,000 of the newer MiG-17s, all of which are dedicated to downing our incoming bombers. Our reconnaissance electronic intelligence, or ELINT, flights probing the Soviet Union since 1946 have encountered increased ability of the updated Soviet radar installations and fighter planes. It can find, track, and intercept intruders. NATO believes the latest version of Soviet radar, the P-10—designated Knife Rest B— is quite good at a distance of 120 to 150 miles and will find anything under 50,000 feet. The VHF frequency, sophisticated anti-jamming, and cluttering suppression capabilities are greater than the Pegmantit 8. Although we do not believe this new system is fully operational, it will be by the end of the year. They are in the process of coordinating their first generation of surface-to-air missiles—or SAMs as we know them—with their radar but are not there yet. There are gaps in their coverage we can exploit, especially on a polar approach."

Caleb paused and took a sip of water. He didn't need it, but he could tell his audience was reeling and needed to breathe.

"We have received what the Agency believes to be credible information from one of our ground assets behind the Iron Curtain that Stalin is planning a wide offensive across a 630-mile front stretching from northern Germany to northern Italy. Some of the Soviet Union's frontline divisions have been pulled back 50 miles to the east and have been replaced by reserve or second-line units. We have long believed the Soviets expected a large-scale conventional war will follow any nuclear conflict. In addition to the troop movements, additional short-range bombers and fighters have been relocated to the approximately 200 air bases within 100 miles of what would be the combat front. We have identified numerous fighters, torpedo planes, and bombers in Albania that we believe will be used to assault the 6th Fleet in the Mediterranean. Submarines from the

Baltic and Black Sea navies are present in large numbers in the Mediterranean. There is also the possibility that Stalin is planning to start with a more limited war anywhere along this front and take what he can get as long as he does not provoke a nuclear response from NATO."

Another sip. Caleb knew a captive audience when he saw one. He flashed back to the enraptured looks on the faces of Princeton students when Dr. Einstein lectured.

"At the other end of the spectrum," Caleb added, "we have what we believe is the less likely possibility—general war. If a general war is being planned, we need to know the Soviet Union's ability to deliver nuclear weapons to the mainland of the United States. We believe the Russians have a limited supply of fissionable material. We estimate that they have 120 30–100 kiloton nuclear bombs. The quantity of fissionable material utilized to produce one bomb has a corresponding effect on the size and number of other nuclear bombs. Although it is unlikely, the Soviet Union could have produced several smaller nuclear bombs or a few larger bombs. Some bombs may be as large as 500 kilotons. We do not believe that the USSR has conducted any thermonuclear tests on anything like this, so stockpiling is unlikely."

No one in the room seemed consoled. Tension was evident, which bolstered Caleb to go on.

"So just a little history on the Soviet Air Force before I get into their present capability to deliver a nuclear bomb to the CONUS. By the early 1950s, the Soviet Union's Air Force was split into three sections. One was in the Far East, the other two—the strategic strike force—stayed in the western USSR. As of January 1, 1953, the Russians had close to 950 Tupolev Tu-4s (code named 'Bull' by NATO). They are reverse-engineered copies of the Boeing B-29 Superfortress Tu-4s.

"Under normal operational conditions, the combat radius is 1,700 nautical miles. The combat range (with a 10,000-pound bomb load) is 3,100 nautical miles. It can reach speeds of 175 knots at 10,000 feet, though it's capable of 347 knots at 32,500 feet for short intervals. Similar to the B-29B, the Tu-4's takeoff weight can be reduced by 2,600 pounds. That increases its combat radius to 2,150 nautical miles and overall range to 4,000 nautical miles carrying a 10,000-pound bomb. We believe that at least five and as many as ten regiments have been so modified. We do not believe the Soviets have more than twenty Bulls modified for in-flight refueling. That would pose a significant threat to the CONUS, increasing the Bull's combat radius to 3,000 nautical miles and its combat range to 5,600 nautical miles."

Caleb paused and encouraged his audience to take out their notepads and record some specific details about the three bases. He emphasized how important it was for them to remember this information.

"Let's start with the Chukotski Peninsula base. This one is important because it's nearest to the United States. If weather permits flights from that area, here are some things to remember when a circle route is used.

"One: The standard Tu-4 with no in-flight refueling could not reach the United States on a round-trip mission.

"Two: On a one-way mission, however, the Tupelovs could reach targets in an arc from San Diego to Lake Superior.

"Three: The stripped-down Tu-4 on a two-way mission could reach Seattle without in-flight refueling.

"And four: A one-way mission without in-flight refueling would permit a stripped-down Tu-4 from Chukotski to reach targets in all parts of the United States except Florida.

"Bombers attacking the United States from northeast Siberia would have favorable tailwinds most of the year. We have identified the following locations where, with proper staging, the Soviet Air Force could support sustained operations despite the harsh climate. They are Markova 65-41N 179-15W and Anadyr/Mys Wizmenny 64-44N 177-33E. Other areas include Velkal, Tanyurer, Magadan, and Petropavlovsk."

When Caleb looked up, he saw that most of the attendees were writing frantically, and he gave them a chance to finish before he went on.

"Now the Kola Peninsula and the Baltic," Caleb continued. "Standard Tu-4 aircraft could not reach the United States and return to their bases even with one outbound refueling. One-way missions present a larger threat. From the Murmansk area, Soviet bombers with no aspirations to return home could reach targets roughly north and east of a line from Charleston, South Carolina, to southern Oregon. From the Baltic area, the line extends from Charleston through Montana. All the northwestern industrial centers of the United States are susceptible from either launch area.

"I believe the Alakurtti-Murmansk (A-M) offers the most likely staging area due to logistics. The circle routes from A-M avoid initial overflight of nations friendly to the United States, whereas those from the Baltic–East German area pass over portions of Western Europe or Scandinavia and risk early detection.

"The CEP—that's the circular error probability, the radius that 50 percent of all dropped bombs or launched weapons will land—of the Tu-4s and Il-28 light jet bombers hover between 3,000 and 5,000 feet. Initial attrition rates run as high as 20 to 25 percent without any consideration of interception and navigational error."[15]

Caleb surveyed the room and continued. "I assume you've all digested the essential elements of the three reports included in the materials you received—the WSEG Interim Report on the Evaluation of Air Defense Weapons and Systems, the Rand-227 Study, and the Final Report from the Lincoln Laboratory."

No one in the room dared admit to skipping the weighty reports. Caleb knew many of them had.

"The handout contains short summaries," Caleb said. "They all reach the same conclusion—we are unable to stop nuclear weapons from being dropped on this country's retaliatory forces. The Rand Study states, and I quote:

In the event of a mass raid of hundreds of bombers, the attrition that our interceptors could inflict would probably be of the

order of 15 percent, but only if adequate warning of the attack were received and if the attack came at high altitude. Against a low-altitude attack in the 1953 period, the Interceptor Force would be much less effective . . . and the major burden of low-altitude defense would fall on 90-mm and 120-mm guns, Skysweeper AA Guns, and on automatic weapons. It is estimated that with the number of these weapons presently programmed for use in 1953, the attrition inflicted on a determined force attacking at low altitude would be very low.[16]
"Consider that carefully."

A voice near the back said, "So we're screwed."

Eisenhower glared. Caleb continued.

"The Lincoln Laboratory Report estimates that twenty atomic bombs dropped on certain population centers in the Northeast would result in more than 10 million deaths. Hundreds of atomic bombs dropped on population centers would result in an estimated 20 million deaths. It continues: 'A single successful raid could overcome the strategic advantage provided by geography and deprive the United States of both the workers and the industrial base required to fight a long war.' The report also asserts that the Soviet Union will soon have the ability to deliver such a crippling blow to the United States. Furthermore, the United States lacks the defensive capabilities to withstand such an attack, and the willingness to construct them has yet to be attained. The most important task of such a defense lies in preventing a tactical surprise."[17]

This time, there was no comment.

"Based on the foregoing, until such time as we can provide an early warning system, I recommend that our Defense Forces operate at a heightened level of alert until we determine if the Agency's intelligence is dependable. Over the long haul, we must develop a distant early warning system as contemplated by Rand Memorandum 1031."

There were mumbles of assent, but no one offered any tangible solution.

"My next topic deals with the employment of tactical nuclear weapons, or TNWs, in support of our NATO troops in Western Europe. The Agency believes that a more likely course of action for the Soviet Union at this point is to attempt to take over West Germany, Italy, and France in a blitzkrieg-type action designed to avoid triggering a nuclear retaliatory action by the United States. Moscow senses reluctance on the part of America's civilian leaders to enter into another general war. Therefore, I believe it is incumbent upon us to revisit the conclusions of Project Vista.

"I am not casting aspersions on anyone in this room or anywhere else. Still, I believe it is vital for us to stage the tactical nuclear weapons we have so they can be utilized when appropriate and necessary. A strategic bombing campaign is, in my opinion, contraindicated since it will most assuredly lead to general war. Before we go there, I want to briefly review the tactical nuclear weapons we can now utilize for the defense of Western Europe."

Eisenhower stood. So did everyone else.

"We've got old bladders and prostates the size of bowling balls," Eisenhower said. "Ten-minute break. Not one second more."

DDI Amory came over to Caleb during the break and tried to remind him not to skip the fact that the Atomic Energy Commission (AEC) had developed tactical nuclear weapons that would offset the conventional superiority the Soviets had.

"Deputy Director," Caleb said quietly to Amory, "I can assure you that they will get all the details on those weapons as soon as they return from the urinals."

Brilliant, but he sure lacks tact, the Deputy Director thought as he returned to his seat, wishing he'd said nothing to the genius. At exactly the ten-minute mark, all were back in the room. Eisenhower nodded to Caleb to continue as General LeMay slumped into his seat and stared at the ceiling.

Caleb picked up his narrative immediately. "In the two years leading up to the project Vista study, the Atomic Energy

Commission has become very adept at producing smaller fissionable nuclear weapons such as the Mark VII nuclear bomb and the W-9 artillery shell, the latter of which has a range of 18 to 20 miles when fired out of an M-65 atomic cannon and a yield of 15 kilotons. As of this date, we do not have any M-65s in our inventory but should be able to deploy twenty or so by the end of this year at the latest. The cannon will be transported by two specially designed tractors. It can be assembled in twelve minutes and torn down in fifteen. The twin tractors can reach speeds of 35 miles per hour.

"The third weapon in development is the MGR-1 Honest John Rocket. It will be mounted on a truck bed with setup taking about five minutes. It is scheduled for a W-7 nuclear warhead with a variable yield up to 20 kilotons and a range up to 15.4 miles. These are very impressive developments in the field. The latest W-7 nukes only weigh 1,680 pounds and can be delivered using the toss system in conjunction with our Low Altitude Bombing System (LABS) by thousands of our planes."

Eisenhower did not speak—a sign to continue.

"Project Vista was a broad joint academic and military study involving fifty preeminent outside scientists populating fifteen study groups," Caleb stated.

This guy is not lacking in self-confidence, Eisenhower thought.

"We produced a final report proposing solutions for the defense of Western Europe. It employed existing conventional forces augmented by tactical nuclear weapons. The dominant military view of the Air Force and Navy was that successful strategic nuclear bombing was the goal to be attained as a response to Soviet aggression involving an invasion of NATO space. The study revealed the opposition that US citizens and their representatives in Washington, DC, had for dependence on strategic bombing. The study concluded that the only realistic way to deliver tactical nuclear weapons for the foreseeable future on critical targets was through the development of ten Air Force attack wings. The other conclusions were as follows."

Caleb leaned toward his binder as if to read, although Amory and Eisenhower knew he'd memorized the entire report.

"I'll begin," Caleb said.

The Air Force wings should be outfitted with the Mark VII bomb with yields from 8 to 61 kilotons. With its weight of less than 1,700 pounds, the Mark VII could be carried under the wings of F-84G Thunderjets and the Navy's fifty specially modified F-2H-2B Banshees, as well as the English Electric Canberra.

It was critical for NATO forces to control the air war above the area of hostilities. Consequently, the fifty air bases supporting Soviet Bloc jet fighters along the frontlines received first targeting priority, followed by forward supply depots.

While a Strategic Attack would cause irreparable harm to countervalue targets, it would not stop the Soviet Bloc's ability to wage war because the SAC did not have adequate mapping to target the Soviet Union's counterforce targets. All of NATO's European population centers would face immediate nuclear retaliation.

Strategic bombing would not stop the Soviet Union's armies' advance before it had conquered all of Europe.

Caleb looked up. "This study was signed off by numerous influential scientists, including Robert Oppenheimer. On December 6, 1951, at the Fontainebleau Hotel in Paris, Professor Oppenheimer met with Eisenhower, who was SACEUR at the time. General Norstad attended. Oppenheimer argued for a measured and flexible response to a conventional Soviet attack. He did not see the need for an automatic strategic bombing campaign or for a general war. If the conventional forces in Europe received support involving tactical nuclear weapons delivered by ten attack wings utilizing a low-altitude bombing system, there would be no need for a strategic bombing campaign."

Caleb paused for effect.

"Finish this up in ten, Dr. Young," Eisenhower said.

Eisenhower knew everything about Project Vista and wished he'd pushed harder for it. It was a secondary war plan he could have used if the Soviets pushed forward in Western Europe. The Vista group did not reach any agreement because General Norstad cited budget constraints and pointed out the impossibility of preparing a new crash program involving the creation of ten tactical air attack wings in twenty-four months.

"I do not have a crystal ball," Caleb said. "That's as far out as I can imagine."

Even though the Air Force suppressed the Project Vista report by recalling it in January 1952, General Eisenhower was authorized by the Joint Chiefs to begin planning for the use of tactical nuclear weapons. In the summer of 1952, General Norstad set up a special study group under Colonel Harold Watson. It met at Wiesbaden Air Force Base in Germany and operated under the code name Whiskey. The study resulted in the targeting of several key Soviet counterforce targets by tactical nuclear weapons. But the Air Force fought the plan, and it wasn't as robust as Eisenhower wanted.[18]

"The final topic I will cover today is one that is largely ignored by the military leaders of this country," Caleb said. "What will be the effects of a nuclear war, even one that is limited to Europe? It has been a little more than seven years since the *Enola Gay* dropped an atomic bomb with a 15-kiloton yield on Hiroshima in the early morning hours of August 6, 1945. Perhaps we have forgotten about the utter devastation caused by a single nuclear device and never completely grasped the destructive capability of what is now considered a low-yield tactical weapon. Remember, we now have the capability of dropping as many as 200 *tactical, not strategic,* atomic weapons— bombs up to four times more powerful than the one dropped on Hiroshima. In case you've never studied the Hiroshima situation, let's review it.

"There was a fireball more than 3 miles in diameter. Within nine seconds, 100,000 people died or were so injured that they expired within twenty-four hours. Over the next three months, another 30,000 died. The total grew to 200,000 within five years—you know that radiation is nasty stuff. Its debilitating effects will ultimately be measured in decades.

"Military leaders, politicians, and even scientists are either oblivious or desensitized to the immense capabilities of the weapons. Now they are theorizing the use of atomic weapons on a massive scale. Robert Oppenheimer could not convince policymakers that a demonstration of the powerful nature of tactical nuclear weapons would bring shock and terror to the Soviet Bloc armies and cause them to halt any advance against Western Europe, which would obviate any need for strategic bombing. Yet it appears that we politicians and policymakers are coming around to his way of thinking—at least that is the indication of Whiskey."

Eisenhower held up his hand. The lecture stopped. For the next two hours, the President, Secretary of Defense Charles Wilson, Secretary of State John Foster Dulles, Chairman of the Joint Chiefs of Staff General Omar Bradley, Air Force Chief of Staff Hoyt Vandenberg, SAC Chief General Curtis LeMay, and SACEUR General Matthew Ridgeway went back and forth. They determined to transfer the Mark-VII tactical nuclear weapons under the control of the Strategic Air Command in French Morocco at Ben Guir, Nouasseur, and Sidi Slimanc air bases to locations in Western Europe and England where they could be utilized by F-84G Thunderjets and the 50 F-2H-2B Banshees. These TNWs were also deployed to Sculthorpe in Britain for use by the English Electric Canberra.

President Eisenhower promised to answer any request for TNW utilization within three hours. Near the end of the session, General LeMay started to grind on the lack of CIA information concerning the location of Soviet counterforce targets.

Caleb felt compelled to answer. "General LeMay, I doubt you are acquainted with Colonel Richard Leghorn. If you were, you would not be blaming the Central Intelligence Agency for a lack of mapping or targeting for your bombers. Colonel Leghorn is a Massachusetts Institute of Technology graduate in aeronautical engineering. During the Second World War, he commanded the Army Air Force's 67th Reconnaissance Group. He was an employee of Eastman Kodak both before and after the war. He was recalled for Korea and made the head of the Reconnaissance Systems Branch of the Wright Air Development Command (WADC) at Dayton, Ohio, in April 1951. We all know the MiG-17 struggles to reach 50,000 feet and is not an effective interceptor at that altitude. We are also fairly sure that Knife Rest A cannot track anything over 32,000 feet. Reliable intelligence reveals Knife Rest B's inability to track anything over 50,000 feet."[19]

Eisenhower interrupted. "Dr. Young, how dependable is that intelligence?"

"Mr. President, without divulging the source, I assure you it is very accurate. Anything we deploy at over 60,000 feet will not be detected by the present Soviet radar systems. But we assume their capacities will improve within the next four years."

Eisenhower was satisfied. "Proceed, Doctor."

Young did not hesitate. "The English Electric Canberra as modified and put into the air as the PR3 can fly at 62,000 feet at a speed of nearly 500 miles per hour with enough range to cover 85 percent of the Soviet Union from NATO bases. In July 1951, its maximum altitude was 48,000 feet. Colonel Leghorn invited the English Electric representatives to Dayton to help find ways to increase the craft's ceiling. As a result, the plane reached 62,000 feet last year.[20]

"The Air Force is cross-licensing the Canberra as our B-57 medium bomber. The PR3 has aeronautical characteristics similar to a sail plane. With a declining fuel supply, it can cruise at over 67,000 feet. Colonel Leghorn persuaded his superiors in the Air Force to submit his idea for our RB-57 to the Pentagon for funding. He had not cleared his idea with the Wright Air Development Center (WADC) or the Air Research and Development Command (ARDC) in Baltimore,[21] which was headed by Lieutenant Colonel Joseph J. Pellegrini.[22] Since the airplane would have been capable of only performing one mission—reconnaissance—changes were made that destroyed its ability to reach even 50,000 feet."

LeMay lost it. "Mother of God! You CIA spooky types are ridiculous. You spend taxpayers' money like drunken sailors on shore leave. The President wants solvency and safety, and the American people deserve fiscal responsibility. We cannot squander our budget on single-purpose airplanes. It's like going into battle with one eye closed."

If LeMay intended to intimidate the scientist, it did not work.

"General LeMay," Caleb responded, "we have no intelligence assets on the ground to provide targeting information for your bombers. Remember, the Russians lost more than 20 million people in World War II. They don't care how many bombs you drop on their civilians. After a nuclear exchange, they believe they will win a conventional war. Unless you can locate and decapitate their counterforce assets, you will not cut off the head of the snake. Once again, we are completely blind regarding the counterforce targets. Our so-called limited use aircraft gives us at least a little vision. What was it Erasmus said? Oh yes, 'In the land of the blind, the one-eyed man is king.'"[23]

Out of the corner of his eye, Caleb saw the President stifle a chuckle.

With his legendary control, General LeMay began to shout. "If you think your f—" (he looked at Eisenhower and decided not to curse) "your ridiculous reconnaissance plane is going to do what you say it will, then take the money out of your budget over at the Central Intelligence Agency. The Air Force will not fund your farce. We can barely afford to do all the things you are already proposing—strategic bombing, interdiction functions, tactical strikes. You want us to pay for everything!"

The veins on the sides of LeMay's neck looked like high-tension cables. His face had turned an odd shade of purple.

"Curtis, sit!" Eisenhower's voice was calm and quiet but left no room for doubt about who was in control of the room.

Well-trained retrievers take more time sitting down than LeMay did. Seething and sullen, he stared at the opposing wall as if searching for his lost dignity.

Caleb informed the group that Russia was producing an estimated thirty Tu-4s per month. The Russians emphasized counterforce targets—SAC bases followed by industrial targets. They also chased the development of a heavy jet bomber along the lines of the US B-52.

The more bombs the Soviets developed, the more they could deliver.

More kilotons.

More destruction.

More death.

∽

April 1964
Office of William Forde, Esq., Chief of the Criminal Division and CIA Liaison
950 Pennsylvania Avenue, Suite 710
Washington, DC

Forde tapped the end of his pen against his teeth. "So the Agency and everyone else had wildly overestimated Soviet bombers and their ability to deliver atomic weapons. At the same time, you underestimated the capacity of Soviet radar to detect planes above 60,000 feet. Right?"

Caleb leaned back in his chair, much like a chess master who can foresee checkmate. He didn't look up from his notes.

"Espionage is not an exact science," he said. "Sometimes there's speculation."

"You mean guesswork," Forde said. He was enjoying the moment. "Doesn't sound very scientific."

"It's not," Caleb said. "If I told you to guess a word ending in the letters o, u, l, and d, I bet you $20 you would not get it right. What would your answer be?"

"Would or could, I guess," Forde said.

"Not bad. Reasonable. But it could be mould, gould, nould, or bould."

"Some of those aren't even words," Forde said.

"Well, gould is a little duplicitous since it's usually a proper noun. Mould and bould, though alternate spellings, are exactly what you think. And nould is an obsolete form meaning 'would not.' Still, you would be wrong, and you would owe me a Jackson."

"Sounds like cheating to me," Forde said.

"No. Sounds like the world of counterintelligence. There are always nuances, interpretations, and—frankly—guesses. We take the best information available and arrive at a reasonable determination."

"Okay. You've made your point."

"Apology accepted."

Before Forde could protest, Caleb continued. "Between 1950 and 1952, we lost several reconnaissance planes. Figuring out that we needed a high-altitude plane did not take a degree from Princeton."

My God, this guy is insufferable, Forde thought.

Caleb read the Assistant U.S. Attorney's expression. "Take a joke, counselor. Take a joke."

Forde, a little embarrassed by his transparency, nodded. "Go back and finish up the NSC meeting on the 29th. My notes show that you and LeMay weren't quite done exchanging pleasantries. Go on with your spy plane stuff."

Forde is loosening up some, Caleb mused. *Might be a human behind those spectacles after all.*

∽

January 29, 1953
National Security Council Meeting
The White House
Washington, DC

"I have every confidence in SAC," LeMay assured everyone. "It could preempt any attempt to strike the continental United States."

"General LeMay," Caleb responded. "There are several obvious flaws to your plan. You do not know where the Soviet Bloc might have its heavy bombers located at any given time. If you are not going to coordinate a preemptive attack with our NATO allies and utilize tactical nuclear weapons for the destruction of the Soviet ground forces, it will be hard to disguise our action as an ordinary military exercise."

Expletives and indecipherable shouting filled the room.

"Enough!" President Eisenhower said in a commanding voice. "It all boils down to a single issue. We are in desperate need of a high-altitude reconnaissance plane."

The President stood. Everyone stood. The President left the room.

∽

April 1964
Office of William Forde, Esq., Chief of the
Criminal Division and CIA Liaison
950 Pennsylvania Avenue, Suite 710
Washington, DC

Forde was supposed to adjourn. It was late. Caleb had already packed his things when Forde decided to take a shot at General Ridgeway. "So the plan of the NSC was to give nearly full autonomy on the monumental decision to use TNWs to a general who would often stand in the middle of the road during World War II with a hand grenade strapped to each shoulder while urinating to show his disdain for the accuracy of the Screaming Mimis. Is that right?"

Caleb almost snapped but reined in a little before replying. "I would not expect a refined gentleman, patron of the arts, and *magna cum laude* graduate of Harvard Law to understand a damn thing about someone like General Matthew Ridgeway or what he accomplished in Europe and Korea to make your family safe. Eisenhower admired and trusted General Ridgeway. He fought his way out of a foxhole. You bought your way out of the service through family ties with the draft board. Before you pass judgment, why don't you grab a rifle and head to Laos and Thailand for what looks like the next Korea? We'll put you in charge of the theater of operations. After you have seen thousands of mauled and dying eighteen-year-old kids, you can criticize Ridgeway, but until then, keep your damn mouth shut."

Forde stared at Caleb like his pants had suddenly fallen off and he was exposed to the world.

Caleb left to cool off over the weekend.

⚬⚬⚬

At their next session, Caleb took some of Eisenhower's policy development programs out of chronological order before he reviewed the next National Security Council meeting that took place on February 4, 1953. He thought it was important to get an overall view of how the President delegated and consulted before making decisions. The Berlin unrest in June 1953 unveiled Eisenhower's empathy for those behind the Iron Curtain. Other developments like the M-4 bomber sighting made him fearful of another Pearl Harbor. Caleb assured Forde that he'd return to the NSC meetings on Operation Mighty Handful before the day ended.

6

May 5, 1953 – 0800 Hours
Sunroom Project Solarium
The White House
Washington, DC

Eisenhower entered the White House determined to cut the 1954 military budget from the excessive levels proposed by the Truman Administration. Joseph M. Dodge, Director of the Bureau of the Budget, and George M. Humphrey, Secretary of the Treasury, were seeking to reduce the 1954 budget deficit by $10 billion. Deputy Secretary of Defense Roger M. Kyes directed the service secretaries to review the military budgets to ascertain where intelligent savings could be made.[24] The military accounted for more than 50 percent of the budget.

With Eisenhower's military background, it was not surprising that he reorganized the National Security Council by appointing Robert Cutler as his National Security Advisor. Eisenhower also redesignated the National Security Senior Staff as the Planning Board with Cutler serving as its chairman. On February 12, 1953, Kyes told the National Security Council that annual defense outlays of $45 billion for the next three fiscal years and $40 billion thereafter were inconsistent with the President's new policies and would not be approved.[25] But the transition Eisenhower envisioned had a few bumps in the road.

Eisenhower backed off proposed drastic cuts when they were deemed inconsistent with the safety of the United States and its allies after General Bradley waved a red warning flag. Along with the Joint Chiefs of Staff, Bradley had reservations about the force level cuts required to balance the budget by 1955. On March 31, 1953, the NSC met with seven outside consultants. They made some progress. The budget and force level targets were set: fiscal year 1954, $43.2 billion; fiscal year 1955, $40 billion; fiscal year 1956, $35 billion; and thereafter, $33 billion. The provisions were designed to maintain an 18-division Army, a 1,200-ship Navy, and 105 to 115 Air Force wings. Eisenhower was making progress on the budget front.

On April 30, 1953, the NSC Planning Board proposed and the NSC approved NSC 149/2, which reduced the Army by 74,000 men and the Navy and Marine Corps together by 70,000 servicemen during fiscal year 1954. The Air Force would be cut by 50,000 by the end of fiscal year 1955.[26] By June 11, 1953, Eisenhower had honed his national defense strategy even further, and the National Security Council approved NSC 153/1. It outlined two principal threats to the survival of the United States:

- The formidable power and aggressive policy of the communist world led by the USSR
- The serious weakening of the US economy that might result from the cost of a continual opposition to the Soviet threat[27]

NSC 153/1 contained a policy statement asserting that the United States must "develop and maintain an offensive capability, particularly the capability to inflict massive damage on Soviet warmaking capacity, at a level that the Soviets must regard as an unacceptable risk in war."[28] In NSC 135/3, the statement was softened. The freshly minted document referred to "the capability to inflict massive damage on the Soviet warmaking capacity." In addition, NSC 153/1 stated that the United States should be "willing to undertake unilateral action, if necessary, against local communist aggression in key areas."[29]

At Secretary Wilson's request, Eisenhower did a full-scale changeover of personnel in the office of the Joint Chiefs of Staff. Admiral Arthur Radford replaced General Omar Bradley as chairman. General Nathan F. Twining succeeded General Vandenberg who was ill and had announced plans to retire effective June 30, 1953. Matthew Ridgway left his post as Supreme Allied Commander in Europe to become the new Chief of Staff of the United States Army, succeeding General J. Lawton Collins. Admiral Robert B. Kearney, Commander of NATO forces in southern Europe, replaced Admiral Fechteler as Chief of Naval Operations.[30]

Throughout all these discussions it was never determined whether the US policy on the containment of communism would be one of containment or liberation, as promised by John Foster Dulles on the Eisenhower campaign trail.

∽

During a meeting in the White House Solarium on May 5, 1953, Caleb Young advised President Eisenhower of a third course of action. The concept became known as "drawing the line." The idea involved tactical nuclear employment followed by strategic use, if required. The "line" around the Soviet Bloc included areas in the Middle and Far East as well as Western Europe. The Cabinet was badly divided. The President and Secretary Wilson created three teams and provided them with the same documentation. Each team worked on a different political strategy.

Team A (Chairman George F. Kennan, C. Tyler Wood, Rear Admiral Harold P. Smith, and others) were to argue containment—with some wiggle room.

Team B (Major General James McCormack Jr., John C. Campbell, Major General John R. Deane [U.S. Army, retired], and others) were assigned to present "the warning of General War" as the primary sanction against further Soviet Bloc aggression. The circumstances under which general war would be threatened had to be defined. Under the policy advocated by this group, the United States would make it plain that any new communist aggression would result in war.[31] There was a line past which the Soviets could not push. Dr. Young was in this group.

Team C (Vice Admiral Richard L. Connolly, G. Frederick Reinhardt, Lyman Lemnitzer, Colonel Andrew Goodpaster, and others) operated on the assumption that the whole enemy structure, dominated by a dictatorial minority, was basically unstable.[32] They were to determine whether the involvement of conceptions and techniques of international action such as subversion, pressure, and threat of force would allow the United States to seize the strategic initiative and deliberately undertake the task of eliminating the communist threat to the free world.[33] This group was to assume that the current of communism was running against the United States and could only be reversed by dynamic, offensive, political action.[34] The mandate for Team C was basically a reiteration of Paul Nitze's NSC-68 that "the United States should diminish Soviet power—Soviet control of territory—by any means available. The United States cannot continue to live with the Soviet threat. So long as the Soviet Union exists, it will not fall apart but must and can be shaken apart."[35]

Eisenhower insisted that the study be conducted at the National War College. The cover story described the work as the first national War College Roundtable Seminar on American Foreign Policy, 1953–1961. The National War College printed conference agendas, booklets, and pamphlets about the seminar to hand out to each team member and to members of the college staff.[36] The report from the three groups was filed with Robert Cutler on July 16, 1953. Major General John K. Gearhart, advisor to the planning board for the Joint Chiefs of Staff, had a negative reaction to the report. He said the proposals were a mixture of policies already in place or had been previously discarded. He suggested a lengthy study of the reasons for the rejection of previously jettisoned policies. The Joint Chiefs of Staff's recommendation to the Secretary of Defense on July 28, 1953, set a six-week time period for the study to be completed.

Eisenhower intervened. He told the council to be ready to discuss the options on July 30, 1953. Although Eisenhower ended up cobbling together a policy like he was ordering food in a Chinese restaurant (one from column A, one from column B), he specifically rejected Team B's proposal for general war based on a specified future action due to its rigidity. He felt the proposal would have a chilling effect on American allies. Even though Eisenhower believed the United States would prevail, he stated, "You can't have this kind of war. There just aren't enough bulldozers to scrape the bodies off the streets."[37]

The policy adopted from Project Solarium was more forceful than Truman's containment idea but less aggressive than the forcible "rollback liberation policy" of Senator Robert Taft of Ohio. There were some areas where Soviet advances would be considered a casus belli, an act provoking war—something by which the United States could justify retribution.

Eisenhower's policy evolved over the years of his presidency. There were at least two opportunities to make good on his aggressive "rollback" policy—East Germany in 1953 and Hungary in 1956. He was wise to pass on both. He knew the world could ill afford a direct confrontation.

He determined that his best course of action was covert destabilization.

7

June 16–17, 1953
East Berlin, Germany

The East German population managed to win a number of concessions from the *Sozialistische Einheitspartei Deutschlands* (SED) (aka the Communist Party) in early June of 1953. On June 10, the communist authorities in East Germany proposed a series of measures involving major modifications, including a promise to halt the collective farm program.[38] There was consideration to restore confiscated property and full civil rights to refugees who returned to East Germany. The SED promised to make state bank credits available to private businesses as well as provide a general amnesty for prisoners guilty of minor economic offenses. It even talked about issuing ration cards to some 250,000 East Germans who had been deprived of essentials.[39]

In retrospect, it was believed the reforms were forced on Walter Ulbricht, General Secretary of the SED, by Moscow in a last-ditch effort to thwart the integration of West Germany into the European Defense League and NATO. But contrary to Moscow's instructions, in addition to the concessions, Ulbricht implemented a 10 percent higher work quota for those with working class jobs such as factory and construction workers without any increase in pay. When government officials refused to discuss the issue, about 5,000 workers walked out of their jobs on June 16, 1953, and took to the streets.

In the United States, the Agency was stunned. Based on a speech by Eisenhower in April 1953 and one on May 11, 1953, by Winston Churchill, it appeared that a Power Four Summit was being agreed upon to discuss the unification of Germany.

Although there were mixed signals coming from Moscow, Lavrentiy Beria looked just like the man behind the curtain. Wilhelm Zaisser, Minister of State Security, and Rudolph Herrnstadt, Editor-in-Chief of *Das Neue Deutschland,* the official communist newspaper of East Germany, had Beria's backing.[40] Because of Ulbricht's failure to implement the reforms in 1952 as dictated by Moscow, Zaisser and Herrnstadt looked to have the votes to oust him. To save his job, Ulbricht made the concessions, but that made the laborers angry, and they remained angry. They were being called on to pick up the slack the concessions caused in the general economy.

Over the next two days, a 5,000-person local protest in East Berlin turned into a 100,000-person revolt. Tanks and tens of thousands of Soviet soldiers were required to quell the unrest. Ulbricht needed a scapegoat because Moscow had not trusted the East German *Kasernierte Volkspolizei,* the KVP, to put down the disturbance and had to send in tanks, which made communism look bad. Although Ulbricht had to backpedal on the 10 percent labor increases, Moscow had to deny the workers' primary demand to have him removed in order to save face for the SED. Back in Moscow where the leadership was in flux, the Politburo took a hard look at Beria's foray into international politics and found it was his plan all along to trade East Germany to the West in exchange for tighter control of the other Eastern Bloc satellites.

The Politburo didn't approve, ultimately costing Beria his life and Zaisser and Herrnstadt any support from Moscow. The Politburo could not remove Ulbricht because such an action might be interpreted as a concession made from weakness and leading to new disturbances with even more far-reaching demands throughout the Eastern Bloc.[41]

Eisenhower got the last word on the world stage when in response to the perfunctory blame case the East Germans laid on the West German government's doorstep, he said, "No provocateur of any nationality can persuade human beings to stand up in front of rumbling tanks with sticks and stones."[42]

Communism had launched a bad ad campaign. To quiet popular clamor, Deputy Premier Ulbricht ordered an increase of consumer production. But the regime was defeated in its efforts to bow gracefully to the demands of the workers. It looked weak. It was telling that the Soviets would not (or could not) depend on the East German police force or the KVP to quell the riots. As many as 125 demonstrators were shot and killed.

From a military or strategic standpoint, the West was helpless since East Berlin was a full 120 miles inside the East German zone. Still, the Eisenhower Administration took some solace from the fact that Eisenhower's April "Chance for Peace" speech might have inspired some sense of nationalism in the East Germans—a possible spark to the revolt.

But the geopolitical landscape was a constantly shifting scene. By midsummer, the Agency had another report that indicated the Soviets were preparing more offensive weapons to deliver nuclear bombs to the United States. The attention shifted quickly to military matters.

∽

July 12, 1953 – 1600 Hours
Ramenskoye, Russia
55 33'12"N 038 9' 6'E

As he drove the embassy car out of the compound's parking lot, Major Martin Manhoff talked to his wife, Jan. The conversation had been meticulously rehearsed. They knew the Soviet GRU was probably listening. Martin followed the directions, 22 miles southeast of central Moscow to the city of Ramenskoye. He had the radio up full blast. Their conversation sounded like two people trying to translate Russian into English.

The drive took a little less than forty minutes. After an hour, Martin saw a large, Russian, four-engine turbo jet with 35-degree swept back wings. The plane descended to a runway while Martin snapped his camera. He jumped back in his car and returned to the U.S. Embassy where he reported his findings to Colonel Charles Taylor, the military attaché. Colonel Taylor took the film and forwarded it to the Agency via the Secretary of State's office.

The Department of Defense and the CIA pored over the grainy pictures. Analysts determined the engines were Mikulin AM-3As. NATO assigned the reporting name Bison to the jet bomber. Eisenhower shared the information with a handful of academics, people who had been warning him of the possibility of a redux Pearl Harbor in 1954.

The Project Solarium study was designed by Eisenhower to quell the discord in his Cabinet between the contain and rollback communism factions. It had been hamstrung by a lack of reliable intelligence on the Soviets' bomber capabilities. Now all that had changed. The photos made those viewing the new Bison gasp.

On May 1, 1954, the Russians formally introduced their new bomber, nicknamed the Hammer, over the skies of Red Square. The Western press hit the panic button. The Russians had in every estimation first-strike capability. Since NATO relied on the SAC as the primary deterrent, hysteria was both predictable and prevalent. After the 1954 May Day show, rumors concerning the new super bomber were perpetrated by the Democrats and the Air Force, along with what Eisenhower would later characterize as "the military industrial complex." US citizens were appalled and terrified. Joseph Alsop and Stewart Alsop published an article in the *Saturday Evening Post* on April 28, 1956, called "The Race We Are Losing to Russia." Similar articles had appeared in *U.S. News & World Report* more than a year earlier before the super bomber appeared.

In August 1953, the Russians had set off their first hydrogen bomb—one far superior to anything in the American arsenal. The Russians had fewer than thirty Bisons but flew them in a circular pattern at a July 1955 air show that gave the appearance of a huge airborne armada. National intelligence estimates from the CIA in 1955 and 1956 estimated that the Russians would have a herd of 900 Bisons by 1960. It's little wonder that Eisenhower felt compelled to build a reconnaissance plane and authorize overflights of the Soviet Union.

America and the American military needed the truth.

Forde, looking impatient, broke in. "Okay, Doctor, thanks for the background on Ike and what was going on with him during his first term. But as you promised, take me back to the NSC meeting on February 4, 1953."

Caleb looked annoyed and felt like Forde had no appreciation for historical insights that shaped the Eisenhower administration's policies. "One more fact you need to know," Caleb said, "so you understand Stalin's death about one month after the NSC meeting on February 4, 1953."

Forde almost jumped out of his seat. "You have my attention, Dr. Young."

Caleb glanced up at the ceiling and decided to let Forde in. "In a joint meeting with MI6 in late January, DCI Smith confirmed British intercepts of a Russian operation called Mighty Handful. He determined that it was merely an exercise that deployed an unusual number of submarines in the Mediterranean. Eisenhower moved the NSC meeting up one day to Wednesday, February 4, 1953, and wanted another full Agency briefing at the meeting."

"So, Doctor," Forde asked, "the Agency had confirmation about Operation Mighty Handful from MI6? But there's still no evidence from you other than Hoxha's diatribe that Stalin was murdered."

"Draw your own conclusions," Caleb responded. "I heard that is what juries do. They weigh the evidence and decide what is and is not credible. I merely report facts. By the way, have you ever investigated why Stalin used the name he did for this operation?"

8

Oval Office
Preliminary National Security
Council Meeting
February 4, 1953

That day, Deputy Director Allen Dulles, Meredith Davidson, Melvin Hendricks, and Dr. Caleb Young had met with President Eisenhower prior to the NSC meeting to discuss the rapid increase in Soviet interceptions within the geographical area of the Eastern Bloc satellites. Caleb was able to reintroduce the idea of overflights with high-altitude planes—crafts able to pass over all the Soviet Union undetected.

Caleb had already been working with the Lincoln Project and the Beacon Hill Group on a camera capable of producing viable intelligence from an altitude of 75,000 feet—day or night. He had also been working with Colonel Richard Leghorn and Major John Seaberg, an Air Force aeronautical engineer who had been recalled to active duty when the Korean War broke out. They were at the Wright Patterson Air Force Base in Dayton, Ohio, and had great ideas about the spy plane, but Caleb knew anything coming out of the Air Force was sure to get bogged down in a bureaucratic nightmare.

The Air Force and Navy had been probing the coastal air defenses all over the Soviet Union gathering ELINT, SIGINT, and COMINT since 1946. They had, on some occasions, been able to penetrate deep inside the Soviet Union before Soviet radar detection. They had picked up Soviet radar signals as an ELINT. Soviet Air Defense Forces had become much more aggressive in intercepting and even shooting down the reconnaissance planes before they entered Soviet airspace. Caleb had started the presidential briefing with a short history of US reconnaissance efforts.

"On June 13, 1952," Caleb began, "an RB-29 Superfortress was shot down by Soviet fighters over the Sea of Japan, resulting in the death of twelve airmen. On October 7, 1952, our fourth reconnaissance plane in the last three years, a USAF-RB-29 carrying eight crew members, was shot down off the east coast of Japan's northernmost island Hokkaido, which is near the southwestern tip of the Kuril Islands chain.[43] On October 8, another USAF plane, a C-47 in the Berlin air corridor, was intercepted and shot at by a MiG-17. The list I have indicates more than sixty intercepts since World War II.

"A few years ago in 1950, the United States Communications Intelligence Board had a treasure trove of information on the Soviet Union's military, industrial, and rail transport activities. That all changed when the defection of William Weisband was uncovered and necessitated the creation of the National Security Administration. Despite our best efforts since his defection, our intelligence community has not yet reached the level of information we had in 1950. We are in dire need of a high-altitude reconnaissance plane, which I believe will, based on recent camera development, provide us with highly accurate estimations, including but not limited to critical information concerning the location of the Soviet heavy bomber fleet at any one time."

Caleb took a moment to look up and read the faces of those in the room. He was pleased and went on. "Since the security breach, the Air Force and Navy's combined SIGINT, COMINT, and ELINT programs have provided us with a veritable plethora of information concerning the coastal defenses of the Soviet Union and the Eastern Bloc. You will find everything in our report, but nothing as detailed as what was provided by the RB-47B and the four 1948 B-29 ferret flights over Siberia. The reason there haven't been any more flights such as those can be summed up very simply. Soviet radar and air defenses, as well as their intercept planes with the advent of the MiG-17 late last year, have greatly improved.

"I am working with the Beacon Hill study group, which as you know was created when Major General Gordon P. Saville added fifteen reconnaissance experts to Project Lincoln, an air defense project, because the SAC lacked targeting information.[44] A summary of the June 15, 1952, report by the Beacon Hill Group is contained within the 150-page report I gave you last week. I believe it is a matter of utmost urgency for the United States to develop a reconnaissance plane capable of achieving an altitude of 70,000 feet with a range of over 3,000 miles."[45]

Eisenhower circled his index finger in the air. He'd heard Caleb's spiels before and wanted him to move along.

"Yes, sir," Caleb said. "The fact that we have no reliable intelligence exacerbates the current targeting situation. We believe Stalin is suffering from increasingly pronounced paranoia. His condition has worsened since the emergence of the Federal Republic of Germany as a potential launch point for a third war by the Germans against the Russians this century.

"We believe he views the failure of the European Defense Community as a crack in the NATO alliance, one he should exploit without delay. Our senior political officer believes that Stalin does not believe the civilians in charge of our military will want to risk a global war over regional disputes along the East-West divide in Central Europe. The other hotspot of which you are aware is in the Taiwan Straits and the various islands such as Yijiangshan and Tachen. The PRC is in the process of assembling naval forces that we believe will be used for an assault on various islands throughout the region."

Davidson could sense the President approaching his boiling point and quickly interrupted Caleb. "Mr. President, the Air Force believes the key to successful long-range reconnaissance of key Soviet defense installations in the interior portion of Russia can be accomplished with a plane achieving a ceiling of 65,000 feet. The closest match in the NATO fleet is the English

Electric Canberra PR3. Dr. Young has recently reviewed the model with our aerospace engineers at Wright-Patterson. He thinks we may be able to use it for undetectable, high-altitude, reconnaissance missions over approximately 85 percent of the Soviet Union."

Davidson glanced at Caleb, who nodded.

Caleb picked up where Davidson left off. "The RB-57 can serve as a stop-gap measure for high-altitude reconnaissance until the Air Force can come up with a better plane. The Air Force intelligence staff is willing to work with Colonel Richard Leghorn and Major John Seaberg to design our own plane for a longer-term solution."

Ike looked at Caleb. "Dr. Young," Eisenhower said, "I don't remember reading anywhere in my report on you that you have a background in aerospace engineering."

"That is correct, sir. My formal training is as a physicist. But I have taken classes in aerospace engineering at Catholic University. I've had the honor of teaching an advanced class."

"Ever the over-achiever, aren't you?" Eisenhower said.

Caleb made no response to what he assumed was a compliment and went on. "Since I was frustrated by our lack of intelligence assets on the ground, I decided to educate myself about high-altitude reconnaissance. We can achieve our goal, but to be blunt, sir, our efforts to build such a craft is continually frustrated by the Air Force's insistence that any plane serve multiple purposes."

Eisenhower frowned. "I need specifics. Why are you blaming the Air Force? It has produced a number of good reconnaissance planes from which we have received very good information."

Caleb's expression never changed. His voice was calm and even. But Eisenhower's eyes grew wider with almost every sentence.

"Mr. President, we have already wasted a year," Caleb said. "Colonel Leghorn provided the Air Force with a detailed modification of the PR3 in mid-1951 only to see it turned down and then approved more than a year later without changes. You have our 150-page report in front of you. The aerial reconnaissance section begins on page 52. Prior to 1950, RB-47s equipped with electronic Ferret equipment could detect tracking by Soviet radar. They were successful in finding gaps in the Soviet early air warning network. On at least one occasion, they flew 450 miles inland and photographed the city of Igarka in Siberia.[46] Since then, however, Soviet air defenses have exponentially increased in the ability to track and intercept reconnaissance planes.

"You can see the details on subsequent pages. The Air Force insists that we cannot have single-use planes. Colonel Leghorn tried to modify the B-57 with the necessary metrics to overfly the Soviet Union and provide extremely useful information on Soviet bombers and missiles. I collaborated with Colonel Leghorn after he was recalled to active duty and stationed at the WADC where he became the head of the Reconnaissance Systems Program. During a meeting in the summer of 1951 with the engineers from the Glenn L. Martin Aircraft Company and the aerospace engineers from England, we made real progress. We designed a new Canberra configuration with very long, high lift wings and a new Rolls-Royce Avon-109 engine.

"It was a single pilot craft. We calculated that it might reach 63,000 feet on a long mission and as high as 67,000 feet as the declining fuel supply lightened the aircraft.[47] Colonel Leghorn convinced his superiors to submit the design to the Pentagon for funding. He had not cleared the idea with the Reconnaissance Division of the Air Research and Development Command (ARDC) in Baltimore headed by Lieutenant Colonel Joseph J. Pellegrini. The Colonel approves all reconnaissance aircraft designs. He modified the proposed plane so it could perform combat functions as well."[48]

Eisenhower smiled wryly. "Yes, you and General LeMay had quite a disagreement last week. Where do we stand right now?"

Caleb was quick to answer, and he knew just what to say. "Fortunately for us, Colonel Leghorn was frustrated enough by the rejection to transfer to the Pentagon early last year to work for Colonel Bernard Schriever who understands the importance of high-altitude photo reconnaissance. On his staff at the Pentagon are Eugene Kiefer, a Notre Dame–educated aeronautical engineer, and Charles Wienberg, who followed Leghorn to the Pentagon from Wright Field."

Dulles interrupted. "Mr. President, I've known Dr. Young for a very short time, but he does come highly recommended."

Dulles turned to Caleb. "Dr. Young, I certainly hope you can deliver on your promise because if you don't, it might be the end of your career with the Agency. If you take us down this path and it doesn't pan out, politics will demand a body, and it will be yours."

Caleb never changed his demeanor. "Director Dulles, if you and the President back me on this, I can produce. If, however, the development of this plane gets tangled up in a bureaucratic snarl, I can promise you nothing. Currently, our three best planes are merely modifications of aircraft designed to carry bombs. They cannot meet the specifications that aeronautical engineers at Wright-Patterson and I deem necessary to carry off undetected reconnaissance of the entire Soviet Union.

"Colonel Seaberg, an aeronautical engineer with a specialization in turbojet engines from WADC, is working on a design. Along with Leghorn, Kiefer, and me, Seaberg thinks the plane will consistently fly above 70,000 feet with a 3,000 mile range. When you meld a turbojet with a glider sturdy enough to withstand 2.5Gs, we will be well on our way to discovering what is behind that 'iron curtain.' You will soon receive a report from the Science Advisory Committee of the Office of Defense Mobilization produced by Dr. James Killian of MIT and Edwin Land, the CEO of Polaroid. Along with others, they agree with the concept."

Eisenhower's stare had not moved. Caleb took the President's silence as consent to continue. "The United States is at great risk for another surprise attack. We must have the reconnaissance plane I've proposed."

Eisenhower tapped on his desk with his index finger for a moment. "Dr. Young, I'm going to consult with Dr. Killian and talk to Secretary Talbott, General Vandenberg, and General Twining. If what you're telling me is true and your high-altitude reconnaissance plane is feasible, you will have the full cooperation of this office. I don't want some three-page summary from an undependable political hack in Yugoslavia or Italy. I want—no, I demand—*reliable* intelligence. I am going to order our forces in the Mediterranean and North Atlantic to full alert status based on your information from our agents in Italy."

The President's eyes took on a darker, almost malevolent, shade of blue. "Dr. Young, at every meeting over the last six months, you've lobbied for your spy plane. I will study the matter and come to a decision." He paused. "And if you are wrong, God Almighty himself will not be able to help you."

Caleb didn't think it was the appropriate time to say he didn't have time to investigate whether God existed or not.

9

Cabinet Room
National Security Council Meeting
February 4, 1953

Dr. Caleb Young was so intently engaged with Eisenhower over the spy plane matter that he didn't notice that Davidson and Hendrickson were halfway down the hall by the time the President reacted. They'd seen "the look of eagles" before and knew it usually foretold something dire.

Allen Dulles had only recently become Deputy Director and been confirmed as DCI. On the way out of the Oval Office, Dulles walked alongside Caleb.

"I don't even want to know," Dulles said, "but it's your neck on the line, not mine, so do what you feel is best. I'll have Trevor Gardner from Secretary Talbott's office front this operation for you, and he can tell me what I want to know. There are a few hundred million lives on the line here, but from what I hear about you, it's all about the science. The Air Force is going to be screaming about our hijacking their project, so make sure you let Gardner know that we are not interested in how it's done. We only care about the final product. Give LeMay and Twinning all the credit so they don't get their pants all twisted."

"All I needed was the President's assurance to cut the red tape," Caleb said. "Credit is superfluous."

∽

Everyone associated with the NSC meeting on February 4, 1953, knew Mighty Handful was something serious. Both the 6th and the 2nd Fleets went on high alert status.

Rather than call for a Four Power Summit on the issue of German unity, at which time the Soviet Union would reiterate an unacceptable plan and risk total derailment of ratification of the European Defense Community Agreement, the President determined to pursue his domestic agenda instead. He asked for de-escalation of the defense budgets and goals set to improve the world's standard of living through foreign policy.

After several confabs, Eisenhower decided to appeal to the Soviet satellites—subliminally—in his April "Chance for Peace" speech by appealing to their pride and sense of heritage. By the time of the speech, Stalin was dead and the Soviet Union was in a state of destabilization. Secretary of Defense Wilson had anecdotal evidence of continuing aggression toward US planes by the satellite air forces. An F-84E had been downed along the West German and Czechoslovakian border on March 10, 1953.

Stalin had died five days earlier on March 5, 1953. Caleb's update regarding the reconnaissance plane disappeared from the March 11, 1953, NSC meeting agenda. Strategy on how to leverage Stalin's demise took precedence.

And still the aggressive intercepts by the Soviets continued.

∽

March 10, 1953 – 0823 Hours
36th Fighter-Bomber Group, 53rd FBS
Bitburg Air Base
Bitburg, Germany

Since the Bitburg Air Base had just recently opened and tensions over intercepts were at an elevated level, Colonel Thomas B. Whitehouse had arrived ninety days early to take over his new command. Another factor that the Air Force considered was that Stalin had just died, and no one knew who was in charge in the Soviet Union.

"Lieutenant Smith," Whitehouse said, "you and Lieutenant Brown are to intercept and identify any intruders you find near Arnstein, which is just north of Waldmuenchen along the Czechoslovakian border. We have reports that the Czech Air Force is continuing to violate West German air space in that area. Per procedure, the guns on both of your aircraft have been disabled. You are not to engage. Observe and report only. Lieutenant Smith will fly lead, and Lieutenant Brown will occupy the wing position."

Flying at an altitude of 13,000 feet on a bearing of 140 degrees, Lieutenant Smith radioed the control tower at 0959 hours.

"This is Green Leader One," Smith announced. "We are observing two aircraft and are turning on a bearing of 320 degrees. Now losing visual . . ."

A little later. "We have reacquired the two intruders. Three o'clock high. We are now turning to 270 degrees in order to avoid engagement."

The planes were MiG-15s. One, piloted by Colonel Jaroslav Sramek, a Czechoslovakian pilot, fired and hit one of the F-84Es with two 37 mm cannon rounds. Lieutenant Brown had to bail out. The wreckage of the plane was discovered 22 miles across the border in West Germany south-southwest of the German town of Falkenstein. The American pilots had been at a severe disadvantage. The MiG-15 was about 100 miles per hour faster at the top end; its rate of climb was 10,000 feet per minute compared to the 3,800 feet per minute of the F-84. The F-84 was limited to bombing and tactical troop support missions.

Even if the six 50-caliber M3 Browning machine guns on Lieutenant Brown's Thunder-jet had been operational, the F-84 would never have managed to maneuver into firing position. The MiG was too fast and too nimble.

It was like playing dodgeball against a legless person.

The next Soviet aggression was the shoot-down of an RAF AVRO Lincoln RF531 C two days later in the Berlin Corridor. Clearly a new, more aggressive page had been turned in the Kremlin.

❧

March 10, 1953 – 1132 Hours
5th Fighter Regiment, 2nd Squadron
Plzen-Line Airbase, Czechoslovakia

Colonel Sramek recounted the action to his base commander. "I spotted them over Merken. They were well within our borders. When they saw me, they ran, and I pursued. They banked sharply and flew off at full throttle. They might as well have been flying a cow. I positioned and fired a warning shot, but the pilot banked, and the shot hit his backup tank on the right side. Fuel started leaking. He tried to escape to the south. I saw flames coming from his aircraft, so I stopped and headed home."

❧

May 1964
Office of William Forde, Esq., Chief of the
Criminal Division and CIA Liaison
950 Pennsylvania Avenue, Suite 710
Washington, DC

"Similar incidents underscored the need for my pet project," Caleb affirmed.

Caleb could tell Forde was fighting the urge to roll his eyes. Forde hated it when Caleb was spot on.

"The Soviets were obsessed with defense, but the Joint Chiefs were paranoid about an attack." Caleb decided to continue with a little background on some of the key players. "Colonel Leghorn graduated from MIT in 1939 with a degree in physics. He was the commander of the 30th Photo Reconnaissance Squadron from 1943 through 1945. When World War II ended, he rejoined Eastman Kodak where he worked prior to the war. When he was recalled to active duty during Korea, he headed the reconnaissance systems branch at Wright Air Development Center. He met Major Seaberg, an aeronautical engineer who had also been recalled to active service. The Major had been telling anyone who would listen that it was possible to pair a turbojet engine with the latest airfoil designs. The result would be a plane with such a low wing-loading factor and such a high lift-to-drag ratio that it would be able to fly well above the ceiling of the latest version of the Soviet radar. We all thought the Soviets had not upgraded their radar from the models we provided them during the war. We were all wrong. Eisenhower was particularly sensitive about the radar issues because he assumed the Soviets believed our mapping flights were a prelude to a first strike.

"Major Seaberg claimed the wing-loading factor would be less than 250 kilograms per square meter fully loaded with fuel and cameras. He also claimed it was possible for the plane to have a lift-to-drag ratio higher than 20. He gained the attention of General Cabell who was in charge of the Air Force's Air Intelligence Division. The General was very enthusiastic because he knew that the sophistication of the reconnaissance equipment was advancing at a rapid pace. He realized intelligence on Soviet weapons could be gathered even when the camera was 70,000 feet above the target. General Cabell was transferred to the development and planning staff of the United States Air Force at the Pentagon and was assigned as liaison officer with the Project Lincoln Group.

"The group produced the Beacon Hill Report. It agreed with General Cabell and asserted that we had sufficient photographic equipment to carry out the assignment. All we needed was—"

Forde interrupted. "The plane . . . I know . . . the damn plane. It's always about the plane."

Caleb felt himself smile a little. *I'm making progress. I should keep going.*

"Major Seaberg and I were making headway," Caleb continued. "In March 1953, we got a memo from Colonel

Edward H. Porter, who is in the office of Air Force Intelligence, Surveillance, and Reconnaissance. It requested that Seaberg outline specifications for a plane to do undetected overflights of the Soviet Union. Not surprisingly, the Major, the Colonel, and I had very different ideas.

"Leghorn was pretty one-dimensional. He favored the Canberra. While we all agreed the Canberra project represented a nice interim step, Leghorn argued that it would take a long time to get approval for the other entries from Bell Aircraft Corporation of Buffalo, New York, and Fairchild Engine and Airplane Corporation of Hagerstown, Maryland. By the time the plane was developed, he assumed the Russians would be ready to defend it. Colonel Leghorn was practical as well as brilliant.

"He knew building a plane from scratch solely for the purpose of conducting reconnaissance would be anathema to the U.S. Air Force's multi-purpose plane production doctrine. It would take years and be outdated before it was produced. So he insisted that the WADC invite English Electric representatives to Dayton in the summer of 1951 to find ways to make the Canberra fly higher than 48,000 feet. The resulting design was a plane with the potential to fly as high as 67,000 feet with an 800-mile radius. It had the capacity to capture 85 percent of the intelligence targets in the Soviet Union and China from bases around their peripheries. The Glenn L. Martin Aircraft Company was licensed to produce the aircraft as the B–57 medium-range bomber. Leghorn was correct in his time assessment. The turnaround time would be much shorter than if a different manufacturer had started from scratch.[49]

"Leghorn's modification of the B-57 concept was submitted to the Pentagon for funding but had not been cleared with the ARDC in Baltimore, which was headed by Lieutenant Colonel Joseph J. Pellegrini. More red tape."

Forde nodded. He was a man who had lived with red tape most of his career.

"Pellegrini was old school," Caleb said. "He wanted a multi-use plane. Colonel Leghorn got tired of slogging through the bureaucratic quagmire and transferred to the Pentagon in early 1952 to work for Colonel Bernard A. Schriever, Assistant for Development Planning to the Air Force's Deputy Chief of Staff for Development. Leghorn positioned himself perfectly. He was responsible for planning the Air Force's reconnaissance needs for the next decade. He was joined at the Pentagon by Charles F. Wienberg and Eugene Kiefer. Outside the Pentagon, other Air Force agencies such as the WADC Dayton, Ohio, continued their research."[50]

Forde stood. "Dr. Young," he said, "the spirit is willing, but the bladder is full. Let's take a break."

"If you didn't constantly sip water, you would be fine," Caleb said.

If it weren't for the water, I'd be guzzling bourbon, Forde thought. *No one warned me this would be the assignment from hell. This guy never shuts up and repeats information we've covered before. Why?*

But Forde smiled and excused himself.

When they reconvened, Forde asked for a chronology of the U-2. Beginning with November 1952, Caleb obliged. About halfway through, Forde regretted his request.

I didn't think he would tell the story in real time, Forde thought.

Forde took another sip of water and tried to imagine the sweet smoothness of his favorite Kentucky beverage.

⌘

November 28, 1952 – 0922 Hours
Bombardment Branch Office
Wright Field – Dayton, Ohio

Major John Seaberg walked down the hall to William E. Lamar's office. In his briefcase, he carried specifications for a new, high-altitude reconnaissance plane.

"Bill, this is the project I mentioned to you a couple weeks ago," Seaberg said. "Take a look, and get back to me. We don't have any reliable intelligence concerning the offensive abilities of the Soviet Union and its Eastern Bloc satellites. I think this aircraft may provide the solution."

"On it, John," Lamar said. "If this works the way you've been claiming, we'll have an interim tool before the Soviets hit their next technology cycle. I've looked at the Electric Canberra, the modified RB-29s, and even the B-47 reconnaissance model. They are all too heavy. Their wing-loading factors and lift-to-drag ratios are all screwy. Not enough range, not enough altitude. Hope this works."

"Your lips to God's ears," Seaberg said. "We need all the help we can get."

∽

December 3, 1952 – 0946 Hours
Office of William E. Lamar, Chief of
New Development
Bombardment Aircrafts Division
Wright Air Development Center (WADC)

Lamar peered over his desk at a fidgeting Seaberg.

"Relax, Major," Lamar said. "You are onto something here. I have approval to send out requests for proposals. Who has to approve them and to whom should we send them?"

"I hate to say it," Seaberg said, "but everything has to go through that dinosaur Pellegrini. He has to be on board if this is going to move ahead."

"That's *Colonel* Pellegrini," Lamar said. When Seaberg flinched, Lamar chuckled. "But I agree with your summation."

Seaberg relaxed a little. "If the Colonel approves, I don't think we should involve major defense firms such as Lockheed and Boeing. This project demands ultra-uber super secrecy. I think we should go with Bell Aircraft Corporation, Fairchild

Engine and Airplane Corporation, and the Martin Company. We will only be asking for about twenty of these birds. The bigger boys are better suited for mass production."[51]

"And the more production, the bigger the possible security leaks, right?" Lamar said.

Seaberg nodded. "Roger that."

Lamar stood. "Go with your gut, John. I'll cover your six with Pellegrini. Code name for this is . . . uh . . . Bald Eagle."

"I like it," Seaberg said. He walked out of the office.

Lamar clenched his teeth. *It's a good idea,* he said to himself, *but I don't care if you like the code name or not, Major.*

∽

The gears ground slowly. The project plodded through the Air Force's bureaucratic pipeline. By mid-1953 (six months later), Colonel Pellegrini reviewed and approved the plans for a new aircraft designed to operate with a 700-pound payload at an altitude of 70,000 feet.

∽

May 1964
Office of William Forde, Esq., Chief of the Criminal Division and CIA Liaison Washington, DC

"This is where Seaberg, Lamar, and I disagreed," Caleb explained to Forde. "I wanted Lockheed in the mix. Their F-104 fuselage was perfect for a turbojet glider. But Seaberg was insistent. This wasn't going to be an assembly line aircraft, so we deleted Boeing and Lockheed from consideration. By July 1953, the Bell Aircraft Company of Buffalo, New York; the Fairchild Engine and Aircraft Company of Hagerstown, Maryland; and the Glen L. Martin Company were awarded study contracts. The deadline to submit their specs and their plans was January 31, 1954.[52]

"Martin Aircraft Company had the simplest task. All it had to do was modify the B-57 light jet bomber with a longer wingspan and improved engines. All three companies submitted their respective proposals by the deadline. Much to their surprise, the ARDC received a fourth unsolicited proposal from Lockheed. It had been authored by their lead civil aeronautical engineer, Clarence 'Kelly' Johnson. Jack Carter, a Lockheed executive, had been in DC in December 1953 on an entirely different matter. In a conversation with Eugene Kiefer, his longtime friend at the Pentagon, Johnson learned about the bids for a high-altitude reconnaissance plane. Lockheed wanted in.

"Kiefer gave Carter a copy of the specifications. Kiefer ran through the US planes that had been shot down and suggested how the F-104 fuselage might be perfect—if modified."[53]

"Interesting," Forde said, "that Kiefer felt comfortable sharing with a buddy what should have been pretty hush-hush stuff."

"It's Washington." Caleb smiled. "If I scratch your back this year, you might do something for me down the line."

Forde tsked. "No wonder it sometimes feels like we're losing. Someone who does that in Moscow disappears."

"Along with his wife, his children, his parents, and the family dog," Caleb added.

Forde shook his head and motioned him on. "Go ahead," he said.

"The British were tighter lipped about their reconnaissance actions. In the early morning of August 28, 1953, a modified Electric Canberra from the US air base in Giebelstadt, West Germany, did a flyover reconnaissance flight of the missile testing site at Kapustin Yar before exiting south to Iran. The flight was known as WH 726. According to reports from the crew, MiGs tried to intercept at about 47,000 feet. One shot exploded close enough to damage the plane and its camera. The explosion made the camera vibrate—American intelligence—"[54]

Forde interrupted. "In this case, apparently an oxymoron."

Caleb looked at him for a moment without any visible reaction. "Your weak attempt at humor notwithstanding, the photos were deemed of insufficient quality as a basis for strategic bombing decisions. The Agency suspected the Russians knew about the mission. In retrospect, it's a virtual certainty. Of course, you know about the Cambridge Five, the university students who've been recruited as spies for England since the 1930s. Well, when the Cambridge Five were uncovered, it was determined that the infamous Kim Philby was friends with James Angleton, the Agency's counterintelligence officer."

After an intentional, uncomfortable pause, Caleb looked up. "No additional joke about that, Mr. Forde?"

"None needed," Forde said. "Besides, the spy ring was no laughing matter."

"Just so, no telling how many lives it cost." Caleb took a moment to compose himself. He thought about the Agency's memorial wall and the row of stars, an anonymous list destined to grow across the decades. He cleared his throat.

"It's okay to show some emotion, Dr. Young."

"Allergies," Caleb said without understanding why he felt the need to avoid the truth. He went on. "The WADC pressed forward with Bald Eagle. Lockheed's submission got a lot of attention because Kelly Johnson had compiled it. He had an impeccable record, having designed and built the F-80 (the Shooting Star) and the F-104, which was set to be evaluated in March of 1954 and promised a top-end speed of Mach 2. Still, Johnson's design was odd—at least for a traditional Air Force plane."

"How so?"

"Although the fuselage was a stripped-down F-104, it was only stressed to 2.5Gs, had detachable wings and tail sections, and did not have any wheels for takeoff or landing. It substituted a jettison-abled wheel dolly for takeoff and had twin skids protruding from a reinforced belly for landing.

In early March 1954, Kelly Johnson formally submitted the CL-282 design to Brigadier General Bernard Schriever's Office of Development and Planning.[55] Eugene Kiefer liked the design and recommended General Schriever pass it on for approval. Johnson was invited to submit a specific proposal, which was to include the cost for thirty aircraft."

10

April 1954
The Pentagon
Washington, DC

After almost biting it in half, Curtis LeMay took the cigar from his mouth and waved it like a drunken samurai.

"That's not an airplane," he said. "Damn thing looks like a malnourished submarine with wings. You keep going down this road and a lot of boys are going to die in that damned contraption."

The presenters stared bug-eyed while the General cursed each one of them, questioned the legitimacy of their parents' marriage, wondered aloud about their sexual orientation, and went out of his way to insult everything they'd ever done.

"Tell you what, geniuses. I'll slap some cameras in one of my B-36 bombers. It'll get the job done. Besides, it's got guns. And here's a news flash—it's got *wheels*. You deviants are so busy with your cockamamie theories that you've got no idea how to get an air machine back onto God's own ground. Not one of you has so much as plopped his ass in a war plane, and as long as I am in charge of the Air Force, none of you, by God, ever will."

Despite LeMay's fulminations, the CL-282 design reached the WADC by mid-May 1954.

∽∽

In June that same year, Seaberg recommended dropping the CL-282 from consideration. He thought the Bell X-16 and the modified B-57 should be awarded production contracts.

Lieutenant General Donald Putt, Deputy Chief of Staff for Development, examined Lockheed's CL-282 and asked why it had been rejected.

Seaberg's response was quick and decisive. "General Putt, if Kelly Johnson would quit being so stubborn and enlarge the fuselage to accommodate the more powerful Pratt and Whitney J57-P37, I'd give his plane more consideration. Kelly knows damn well that at 70,000 feet the engine will have a 6 percent efficiency ratio, and the larger engine will improve the glide by over 30 miles."

Despite the rejection, Kelly Johnson continued to work on the CL-282. He knew he had the best airplane for aerial reconnaissance. But in September 1954, the Air Force entered into a formal contract calling for the production of twenty-eight Bell X-16s.[56]

⌘

May 1964
The Pentagon
Washington, DC

"Mr. Forde," Caleb said, "I need to take a minor detour here to continue with the development of the U-2 because a lot was going on between Eisenhower and our scientists at our major universities. It all had a direct effect on the development of the U-2."

"Get on with it," Forde said impatiently.

Without hesitation, Caleb continued. "Dulles made Richard Bissell the CIA project manager for Aquatone, the CIA code name for development of the U-2. I had met Bissell years before he became an employee of the CIA in January of 1954. It was during informal gatherings of what was known as the Georgetown Set. Bissell was drafted by Dulles to head Aquatone (Bald Eagle for the Air Force). He was so involved in other operations such as the overthrow of Central American governments that I had to regularly remind him about Aquatone.

"Bissell and I met with Allen Dulles, who was not enthusiastic about infringing upon what he considered to be Air Force turf. But Phillip Strong, the CIA's liaison with the Air Force, reminded Dulles that Eisenhower had been making very extensive use of the scientific community's efforts in endeavors such as the Lincoln and Beacon Hill study groups as well as the Technological Capabilities Panel (the TCP) chaired by Dr. James R. Killian Jr., president of MIT.

"The TCP began meeting on September 13, 1954. Panel Three was in charge of intelligence capabilities and consisted of Edwin Land, James Baker, Edward Purcell of Harvard, chemist Joseph W. Kennedy of Washington University in St. Louis, mathematician John W. Tukey from Princeton University and Bell Laboratories, and Allen Latham, Jr. of Arthur D. Little. Little was an engineer and the former treasurer of the Polaroid Corporation. Even before the TCP came into existence, the Air Force, fearing a sneak attack and acting on the Beacon Hill study recommendations regarding a high-altitude spy plane, created the Air Force Intelligence Systems Panel (ISP) in July 1953."[57]

∞

The chairman of the ISP, Dr. James G. Baker, had established an optical laboratory at Harvard (later moved to Boston University) charged with continuing the effort so long as the Air Force would pay for it. In a meeting of the ISP members on May 24–25, 1954, Allen F. Donovan, a talented engineer from the Cornell Aeronautical Laboratory, reviewed data from the PR.7 Canberra overflight of the Soviet Union. He reviewed the Martin Company's specifications and drawings for the modified B-57 awaiting Air Force approval and compared them to the ones proposed by the Brits for upgrading the PR.3. In the English flight over Kapstan Yar, the Canberra had reached an altitude in excess of 65,000 feet but was still damaged by Soviet air defenses. After making all possible modifications to the B-57, Donovan concluded that the Air Force was about to commit to a "sitting duck of a plane." Baker urged him to travel to Southern California and evaluate the Lockheed aircraft.

On August 2, 1954, Donovan met with Lockheed Vice President Eugene Root and Kelly Johnson. Donovan, a lifelong sailplane enthusiast, immediately recognized that the plane could cruise at an altitude of more than 70,000 feet. When he returned to Washington, he called an urgent meeting of the ISP. The soonest everyone could assemble was September 24. While everyone concurred with Donovan's assessment, it appeared the Air Force had already committed to the other two planes.

They figured not much could be done. When Edwin Land, the brains behind Polaroid, saw Kelly Johnson's conceptual drawings for the CL-282, he was astonished that the Air Force had rejected it. He remembered a conversation with Allen Donovan about a reconnaissance plane. Land did not realize Donovan had meant *this* one. As soon as he saw the drawing, Land got on the phone, called Baker, and said, "Jim, I think we have the plane that we can pair with your camera."

∞

Patience was becoming a scarce commodity. The scientists were frustrated. Members of the ISP and TCP Panel 3 did not understand the nonchalance exhibited by the Joint Chiefs of Staff and the entire National Security Council. The more Land and Baker talked with high-ranking military officials, the more concerned they became.[58]

In a confidential setting, Land said, "Here we were, a half dozen science geeks asking questions of the leaders of our Armed Forces about Soviet military threats, and these guys with enough ribbons on their chests to accessorize an Easter parade have no clue."[59]

Caleb Young was completely in favor of Lockheed's CL-282. Along with others, he felt the best course of action was to move the Air Force to the side and get the CIA behind the craft. Dulles needed a push before anyone went to the President.

∽

"On November 5, 1954, I met with Edwin Land," Caleb told Forde. "We drafted a five-page letter to Allen Dulles in which we implored him to adopt the CL-282 project. We called Eisenhower's office and got on his schedule.

"James Killian was going with us. Eisenhower respected him. Dulles didn't know we were going to see Eisenhower. I wanted to give him time to digest Land's letter. The Air Force continued to insist on the Bell X-16. Seaberg felt it was more airworthy than the CL-282 and could be used throughout the Air Force on various types of missions because it had two engines and a pressurized cockpit. He completely ignored its inability to reach an altitude of 70,000 feet. It would have been a very expensive clay pigeon."[60]

∽

November 1, 1954 – 0800 Hours
Oval Office, the White House

Eisenhower scowled. "So what you gentlemen are telling me is the Air Force has spent about $50 million of taxpayer money on a reconnaissance plane destined to be shot down by the Russians?"

Caleb nodded. Land and Killian did not move. They were gauging the wind.

"And," Eisenhower said, "once it's blown out of the sky, we could be facing another war. That about it?"

"Yes, sir," Caleb said. He didn't bother checking to determine if his compatriots backed him. "A modified bomber will never suffice as a reconnaissance plane, Mr. President. You can use a baseball bat as a fly swatter, but it won't be very effective."

"Well said," Eisenhower said. "A little cute but well said. But what about the Canberra? It was downed through a security leak, was it not?"

Killian recovered his voice. "True, sir, but the leak doesn't matter."

"Pardon?"

"Well, it's important, sir, but the fact remains—the plane could not get above 67,000 feet. No craft will be safe unless it can get to 70,000."

"What leads you to believe that a plane at 70,000 feet will not suffer the same fate?"

Killian's confidence grew. "Mr. President, the Canberra was not shot down. It suffered minimal damage from what is believed to be an incredibly lucky shot by a MiG-17 operating more than 4 miles below where we want our new plane. Without being tipped off, the Soviet air defenses have a very small chance of even detecting a reconnaissance plane more than 70,000 feet up, much less damaging it.

"Our intelligence community is currently operating in the dark. The new plane will be able to find and identify Soviet assets in a 200-mile-wide arc over 2,000 miles inside the Soviet borders. We will be able to tell you not only the number of heavy bombers and missiles the Russians have but also what type of plane or missile it is and where it is located. We have interviewed your intelligence community. Quite frankly, we are worried by the lack of answers available to pertinent questions concerning the defense of our nation. I am sure you are aware of the RAND Report from early 1953 that indicated more than 85 percent of our Strategic Air Command could be taken out in a sneak attack."

Now on a roll, Killian detailed the CL-282 but did not refer to it by name. He wanted to get Ike on board and then flip the

Air Force to the CL-282. All the details about the plane such as the wingspan and sailplane characteristics piqued Eisenhower's interest.

When Killian finished, Eisenhower stretched. "I don't know who you are going to get to fly this thing, but tell the Air Force I like it. I do not want to see the Department of Defense involved because the Navy and the Air Force will be at each other's throats."[61] He turned. "Dr. Young, this operation runs out of the CIA, and none of the pilots should be in the US military."

"Yes, sir," Caleb replied.

Eisenhower tapped a finger on an imaginary budget. "The money comes out of the CIA Contingency Budget because there is no Congressional oversight. This project is top secret. He locked eyes with each of them—one at a time. "There cannot be any leaks."

∽

The Air Force still presented a considerable obstacle. Without its cooperation, the project would slowly . . . but inexorably . . . die. Land and more than a dozen scientists met with General Putt, Major Seaberg, and Kelly Johnson. The project was a money loser because whatever manufacturer won the bid would have to pull its best engineers off more profitable work. The timeline was daunting. In Lockheed's case, the CL-282 would be expected in the air by August 1955.

Seaberg finally accepted defeat. He could not battle the scientists *and* Eisenhower. But he did win one concession. Kelly Johnson agreed to enlarge the fuselage to accommodate a larger engine. Director Dulles agreed to run the operation out of the CIA.

11

June 21, 1932 – 1530 Hours
United States Bankruptcy Court for
the Southern District of California
Main and Temple Street
Los Angeles, California

The bailiff announced the case. "This is the matter of the auction of the Lockheed Aircraft Company by the Detroit Aircraft Corporation. Case number 31-00-96281-RLS. The Honorable Ronald L. Stageman presiding."

The judge looked out over the assembled. "This being the date and time set for auction of the Lockheed Aircraft Corporation, does anyone have a bid to submit to the clerk for reading?"

A woman with her hair in a headache-inducing bun and sensible shoes stood. "Your Honor, I have received one bid from Robert E. Gross in the amount of $40,000."

"Thank you, Mrs. Laerie," the judge said. He liked his clerk—efficient, no nonsense, no frilly presentations. "As we have only one . . . uh . . . contestant, the bid is accepted and certified as the winner of the auction." The judge peered over his glasses at a slender man in a fashionable suit. He had wide shoulders, a narrow waist, and full, almost baggy pants. Mr. Gross, I presume."

"I am, your Honor," the man said.

"If memory serves me, sir, you were the president of the Viking Flying Boat Company."

"Guilty as charged," the man said. He grinned.

The judge did not.

"The company failed, correct?"

"Yes, your Honor."

"Mismanagement?

"Bad timing, sir. The Crash of '29 decimated the aviation industry."

"Well, Mr. Gross, better luck to you in this venture." The judge banged his gavel. "Sold to Mr. Gross for 40,000 US dollars." He looked at Gross. "Be careful what you wish for."

∽

November 21, 1954 – 1316 Hours
Lockheed Aircraft Corporation
Burbank, California

Joan Bismore burst into the room. Robert E. Gross looked up from his meeting with Eugene Root and Kelly Johnson.

"This had better be good," Gross said.

"Sorry, sir." Joan was usually calm and business-like. At the moment, she looked like someone who'd discovered a snake in her bathtub. "You have a call."

"Again, this had better be—"

She didn't let him finish. "It's the President, sir."

"I talk to damn presidents every day." Gross was stressed enough without frivolous interruptions. "President of what?"

"The United States, sir."

Gross took a beat and swallowed. "As in Eisenhower?"

"Yes, sir. I should have led with that, but I'm a little flustered. I've never talked to the President of the United States before."

Gross, now composed, grinned like Alice's disappearing cat. "Better get used to it, honey," he said. "Probably won't be the last time."

Gross picked up the phone. "Good afternoon, Mr. President."

"Thank you for taking my call, Mr. Gross," Eisenhower said politely. "The Chief Science Officer from the Central Intelligence Agency, Dr. Caleb Young, just left my office. I thought it might be a good idea to call to verify that you're agreeable with designing our reconnaissance plane."

"Interesting coincidence, sir. I am discussing the issue with Eugene Root and Kelly Johnson as we speak."

"Wonderful! The Soviet Union is a riddle, wrapped in a mystery, inside an enigma,[62] as Mr. Churchill put it. This project is priority one. Our nation's very existence lies in the balance."

"We will do our best, Mr. President." Gross hoped his gulp had not been audible.

12

January 3, 1955
Advanced Development Division
aka Skunk Works Building 304
Lockheed Aircraft Corporation
Burbank, California

The Skunk Works division got its name while working on the P-38 Lightning. Kelly Johnson had walled off a section of one of the buildings to work on the P-38 in secret. The team was temporarily moved, first to the former 3G Distillery building, which reeked of bourbon mash, and then to a malodorous plastic factory.

Irv Culver, one of the select engineers, referred to the plastics facility as Skonk Works. It was a reference to skonk oil, a concoction brewed by Big Barnsmell in Al Capp's *Li'l Abner* comic strip. For reasons unknown, Barnsmell ground dead skunks and old shoes into a still. The engineers changed the name to Skunk Works at the "request" of the comic strip's copyright holders. No one except Gross ever got to call Kelly Johnson "Barnsmell."

Johnson had a reputation of firing and hiring aeronautical engineers with the regularity of a basketball player changing socks. After monumental screaming matches with supervisors, Johnson and Dick Boehme settled on twenty-five engineers with various specialties. Henry Combs, a structural engineer and sailplane enthusiast, collaborated with Johnson on the critical decision to utilize the Mach 2 F-104 fuselage. Below is the rest of the lineup:

Aerodynamics: Chad Engelbry
Loft Lines: Carl Allmon and Alvin Jensen
Stress Limits: Henry Combs, Ray McHenry, Richard Hruda
Wing Structure: Bob Wiele, Bill Bissell, Robert Kelly,
    Caleb Young, Royal Dow

Hydraulics: Vern Bremberg
Electrical: Sam Murphy, Cliff Rockel

The project was several months behind Bell and Martin. Johnson kick-started things by deleting a 62-inch section of the fuselage just behind the XF-104 cockpit.[63] The move reduced the overall weight by 3,990 critical pounds. Every shaved pound meant another 2 feet of altitude. When Dr. James Baker called Johnson and asked him whether the camera could be 6 inches wider and 10 pounds heavier than the previous specifications, Johnson said, "No. I'd sell my grandmother for 6 more inches of space and 10 pounds."

Johnson eliminated considerable weight by utilizing aluminum alloys machined to the thinnest structural strength allowances. Unlike fighters with 7^+G stress levels, the spy plane was designed for a maneuvering load factor of 2.5Gs. Johnson settled on 80-foot wings with a total surface area of 600 square feet. The distance from the leading edge to the trailing edge (chord line) was 100.8 inches, with a lift-draft ratio of 25:1. The plane could glide at 70,000 feet for 300 miles while burning a small amount of fuel required to maintain a speed of 12 mph higher than the 430 mph stall speed.

The wings carried a total of 1,335 gallons of specially formulated JP-TP jet fuel with a sea-level boiling point of 315 degrees Fahrenheit. At takeoff, until the wings had enough lift to support the weight of the fuel, they were supported by mid-span outriggers (or pogo sticks) with small rubber wheels on the ends of curved, steel legs. The pogo sticks dropped away as soon as the plane became airborne.[64]

∞

May 1964
The Pentagon
Washington, DC

"The outriggers were my idea," Caleb said. "The plane was as difficult to fly as it was to get into the air. Landing was delicate.

The high wing aspect made the plane want to float as it neared the ground. The very low tolerance window between cruising speed and a stall became known as the 'coffin corner.' We had to install gust control features, and that changed the airfoil characteristics."

"Sounds tricky," Forde said. He was on the edge of his seat like a kid watching a Saturday matinee Western.

"It was."

"So the pogo sticks were your idea?"

"Yes. I was sort of responsible for making them necessary."

"How so?"

"I showed how we could increase the wingspan from 70 to 80 feet. Everything got better—altitude, aspect ratio, lift-to-drag ratio—except the wings would have run along the ground. Not the best idea. Damage, sparks around jet fuel, that sort of thing."

"Ouch!" Forde winced a little at the thought of an expensive fireball on some Air Force runway.

"Anyway, Kelly knew I had something to do with the whole thing. I made my suggestions *sotto voce*, you know."

"Couldn't have been easy for you," Forde mumbled through a smirk.

"Touché. But Kelly knew. In fact, he gave me a gift."

"Your own spy plane?"

Caleb didn't want to, but he laughed . . . a little. "No, there was a very nicely wrapped present on my desk. I opened it in front of the entire crew. There was a massive cheer."

"Let me guess," Forde said. "A real pogo stick."

Caleb smiled. "Given my height, it was a little small, and it looked like something on which I could easily be injured, so I gave it to Bob Weil. I understand his children enjoyed it very much, but his wife was not happy about the damage to the house they inflicted while they were learning."

Forde and Caleb both smiled a little. Anything remotely resembling friendship or camaraderie made them both uncomfortable. After a while, the moment passed, and Caleb went back to a recitation of the plane's construction.

"There hadn't been a written contract, and Lockheed received no payments for the first six weeks. Everything was very hush-hush. The first check finally came. It was for $1,256,000, mailed to Johnson's home.[65] Kelly Johnson was as good as his word. He'd promised delivery in eight weeks. The disassembled components were delivered to the Watertown Airstrip north of Las Vegas on July 25, 1955. On August 1, 1955, the first plane, called Article 341 by Lockheed, taxied down the runway with the corporation's premier test pilot at the controls.

"As designed, Article 341 was to lift off at 90 knots and land at 76 knots. Tony LeVier taxied down the runway. At 45 knots, the wing tips began to lift; however, the pogos remained locked in place. LeVier put the plane back on the ground and started back the other way. At 70 knots, he pulled the throttle back to idle, but the plane lifted off the ground. The only way he could land it caused the plane to bounce. The plane caught fire. The blaze had to be extinguished by the chase vehicles, a rather inauspicious start for Article 341—what we now know as the U-2."

Caleb was proud of the mind picture he had created for Forde. He could see that Forde had enjoyed his very descriptive account of the Article 341 debacle.

"LeVier continued to work with the airplane until he and Kelly Johnson were satisfied that they were ready for an audience," Caleb continued. "On August 8, 1955, the CIA leadership, Air Force brass, and Lockheed officials witnessed a successful test flight. By September 8, the U-2 had reached an altitude of 65,000 feet. The J57-37 engine exhibited major problems. Chief among them were flameouts at higher altitudes.[66] This problem persisted until Pratt & Whitney developed the J57-P-31. They turned everything around in ten months, one-third the normal time."

"I guess you hurry when the fate of the nation is at stake," Forde said.

"Indeed." Caleb, who never needed notes, kept his eyes on Forde and never looked down. He went on with his story. "In

November of 1955, Colonel William R. Yancey, Curtis LeMay's handpicked representative, evaluated the program. When he first saw the plane ready for takeoff, he turned to Major Peter Howard who had accompanied him and said, 'Where is the big top tent for this circus? I think Dumbo's got a better chance to fly than that plane.' But by January 11, 1956, he greeted the first group of pilot trainees at Watertown. They were all former F-84 pilots. At their briefing, he didn't pull any punches. He announced that some of them would die trying to master the airplane."

"He should have been a motivational speaker," Forde said.

"You have a point," Caleb said without smiling, "but he wanted everyone to have their eyes wide open. This was not a walk in the park. The U-2 was the very definition of an experimental craft."

"Anyone die?" Forde asked.

"Yes. These were the best—Air Force trained. Still, three of them lost their lives despite the fact that Lockheed had sent a two-seater plane that allowed the trainer to ride with the new pilot."

"Those test pilot guys were either brave or crazy," Forde said.

"Could be a little of both," Caleb said. "Regardless, the clock was ticking. In April of 1956, Colonel Yancey met with Donald Quarles, the Secretary of the Air Force, and Nathan Twining, the Air Force Chief of Staff. They determined the plane was ready for deployment overseas. Detachment A was deployed to Lakenheath Air Base in England in mid-April."

∽∞∾

1955

Internal Cabinet battles continued to pressure Eisenhower's need for better intelligence while world events kept catching the Agency unawares. It did not foresee either the uprising in East Berlin or the development of the Bison and was roundly (and justifiably) criticized for its myopia.

The post-war world was different from the one before Pearl Harbor. Technology was beginning to open up new vistas—areas of development never imagined in the sleepy and globally disinterested United States of the 1930s. The Great Depression (and the national angst over World War I) had turned America inward until December 7, 1941, when the events at Pearl Harbor dragged an enraged nation into another maelstrom of violence and death. After Hiroshima and Nagasaki, citizens from Maine to California wanted nothing but rest . . . and peace.

After the Second World War ended, only a comparative few kept watch, and they could not see everything at once. Too much was happening too fast. It was as if someone had switched the global phonograph from 33.3 to 78 rpm.

13

April 29, 1956
4070th Support Wing U.S. Air Force
RAF Air Base
Lakenheath, England

Richard Bissell and Colonel Yancey were planning overflights of the Eastern Bloc satellites when several incidents made Detachment A *persona non grata* in the United Kingdom. For starters, Bissell had informed Prime Minister Anthony Eden that only one U-2 had been shipped to England. In truth, four of them were assembled. To make matters worse, on May 1, 1956, a U-2 training flight drifted into restricted airspace where it was spotted by British radar. The RAF scrambled fighters to intercept the intruder. The British Air Ministry had to cobble together a cover story to protect the top-secret new plane. It announced that a special National Advisory Committee on aeronautics was conducting high-altitude research over the United Kingdom. To make matters worse, a couple of weeks before the 4070th arrived in England, the British had an embarrassing international incident involving Khrushchev and one of their spies.

∽

April 19, 1956 – 0337 Hours
Portsmouth Harbor
Hampshire, England

Terrence Whittington of MI6 gave parting instructions to the operative. "Buster, to review, you are to dive to 150 feet and investigate the Ordzhonikidze's propellers. The Royal Navy thinks this Sverdlov-class cruiser has a newer design that will increase the speed of the Soviet's blue water Navy by more than 20 percent. You are to spend no more than 15 minutes beside the cruiser. You cannot be spotted. Security is very high. Premier Khrushchev and Nikolai Bulganin are on a state visit and are scheduled to sail on the craft. Do not dally."

"Roger that, sir." The wrinkles around Lionel Crabb's eyes deepened when he smiled, and he always smiled before a mission. The British Navy frogman, nicknamed "Buster" in honor of American swimmer and *Tarzan* actor Buster Crabbe, had been diving for fifteen years. Though the mission required stealth, it was hardly the most harrowing of his distinguished career.

He spit into his mask, rinsed it, and nodded to Whittington. "I'll be back in less than thirty minutes."

Crabb was never seen alive again.

When a headless, handless body matching Crabb's general description was recovered by a fisherman, Anthony Eden sent a letter to Eisenhower requesting a delay in all Eastern Bloc overflights. The 4070th packed up and headed for Wiesbaden, Germany.

During the delay, the J57-31 engine replaced the J57-37 engine, which reduced the risk of a flame-out at altitudes over 60,000 feet. The delay also gave the CIA time to have the National Advisory Committee for Aeronautics, the predecessor to NASA, issue a press release indicating airplanes capable of reaching 55,000 feet would be conducting data-gathering flights in the United States and Europe to study weather patterns.[67]

Bissell was all set up to begin his overflights. Eisenhower was still reluctant. Regardless, Bissell scheduled the first flight for June 20, 1956.

Eisenhower had never been comfortable with the idea of the overflights, but he had been inexorably pressured not only by his own national security establishment but also by a relentless onslaught of press articles where hysterical claims announced that the United States was losing the bomber and guided-missile race with the Soviets by a large margin. The first article of note came out on May 23, 1955, in *Aviation Week*. The article title was "Russian Jet Air Power Gains Fast on U.S." Articles in *Time* and *U.S. News & World Report* followed suit and added to the national angst. When Eisenhower failed to get Khrushchev's consent on the "Open Skies" policy at the July 21, 1955, Geneva Summit, the President shrugged. "I'll give it one shot," he said. "Then, if they don't accept it, we'll fly the U-2."[68]

When the Soviets fired a missile with a 900-mile range, the Premier boasted, "I am quite sure that we shall have very soon a guided missile with a hydrogen bomb warhead which could hit any point in the world." US paranoia skyrocketed.[69] The Soviet propaganda program continued to pound on the international community's psyche and push the Western world, especially the United States, to devote an increasing amount of resources to weapons as opposed to durable consumer goods. The Soviet economy was in terrible condition. The USSR's gross domestic product was only a fraction of America's. Because of their inefficiencies in mass production, nearly 30 percent of Russian resources were devoted to defense spending.

To his credit, Eisenhower tried to rein in runaway defense spending, but because the Soviets' beguiling bluster plan was so well-executed and the US public was such a gullible target, Eisenhower was pressed into spending tens of billions more on defense than he had originally planned when he came into office. The Soviets were playing a long game—a dangerous one. If the US military had an opportunity, it would not hesitate to launch a preventive attack on the Soviet Union and China. The communist world would be unable to absorb the assault.

While Eisenhower was contemplating whether to go ahead with the U-2 flights, the State Department received a protest from the Soviet Embassy on May 14, 1956, concerning overflights in northern Siberia. Those flights originated out of the US airbase in Thule, Greenland, and were conducted by RB-47 Ds tasked with probing the Soviet air defenses over routes to be used by SAC bombers to deliver nuclear weapons. Bissell intended to assuage any lingering reservations that Eisenhower may have harbored by completing successful, undetected flights over the Soviet Eastern Bloc satellites. No one really knew for sure how good the Soviet radar was. Bissell probably didn't share the Agency's study from his own Office of Scientific Intelligence.

> Maximum Soviet radar detection ranges against the project aircraft at elevations in excess of 55,000 feet would vary from 20 to 150 miles. . . . In our opinion, detection can therefore be assumed. It is doubtful that the Soviets can achieve consistent tracking of the project vehicle.[70]

Dulles was not as coy. He told Eisenhower that even if a plane was lost over Soviet territory, it would be reduced to ashes either from the self-destruct switch or from impact. The aircraft's fragile, birdlike construction would not survive the plummet.

∽

May 28, 1956 – 1430 Hours
Oval Office, the White House
Washington, DC

Dulles delivered the update on Project Aquatone. Eisenhower scowled.

"You know the Russians will view any overflights as recon for a massive first strike," Eisenhower challenged Dulles.

"I can't read their minds, Mr. President, but I suspect you are correct. Still, we have the technology—the planes, the cameras, and the pilots. We can determine the Russians' capacity to attack us, and we would be foolish to bypass the opportunity to garner such vital information."

Eisenhower fiddled with a fountain pen but never took his eyes off the Director. "We still do not believe they are capable of continuous tracking of the U-2. In fact, we don't believe they can even detect anything above 60,000 feet at this time. June and July are the two best months for the overflights. Our intelligence community believes the next generation of Soviet radar, surface-to-air missiles, and planes most likely will not only be able to track but will also have the capacity to bring down the U-2. Our assets believe the developments will be within three years. We suspect the British have been using a modified Electra Canberra to conduct overflights at 64,000 feet. We can fly a mile higher. Since the overflights are a violation of international law, the British will not share their results with us."

Eisenhower turned to Bissell. "Agent Bissell, would you like to share some input?"

Eisenhower put down the pen and nodded, a sign for Bissell to speak.

"Mr. President," Bissell said, "we will be able to detect if we are being tracked. Even if so, the Russians cannot reach our craft in any meaningful way. When we get the film and data, there will be a very quick turnaround."

"You know the Russians are already howling about our weather balloons," Eisenhower added. "And we know they are doing ballistic missile testing in the Kapustin Yar area. At least that's Prime Minister Eden and his intelligence community's best guess. Is the juice worth the squeeze here?"

Bissell blinked. "Pardon?"

"Are we going to learn enough to make the risk acceptable?" the President asked. "We are risking serious destabilization of an already tense relationship."

Eisenhower stood, a signal there would be no more discussion.

"Keep me informed," the President stated. "I'll talk with Secretary Wilson about putting our forces on standby without tipping the Soviets off about any activity. But they are becoming very sensitive to our activities, and I can't say that I blame them. We continue to violate their airspace not only in Siberia but also in Central Europe over their satellite states. Be damn careful, gentlemen. That's all."

Joseph Stalin (1878–1953) led
the Soviet Union from 1924 until
his death on March 5, 1953,
becoming a dictator in the 1930s.
Photo: Public Domain

Nikita Khrushchev (1894–1971)
succeeded Stalin as First
Secretary of the Communist
Party of the Soviet Union
(September 14, 1953, to
October 14, 1964). Khrushchev
spoke in East Berlin on June 3–4,
1961, about the Soviet-German
brotherhood.
Credit: CIA Historical Collections
Photo: Public Domain

Nikita Khrushchev (1894–1971)
in 1959
Photo: Public Domain

Dwight D. Eisenhower (1890–1969), 34th
President of the United States, 1953–1961
Photo: Public Domain

General Dwight D. Eisenhower, Mamie Eisenhower, General
George C. Marshall, and others
Photo: Public Domain

Lavrentiy Beria (1899–1953) led the Soviet Union after Stalin's death for three months. Nikita Khrushchev and Georgy Zhukov removed him from power in June 1953. Beria was tried for treason and executed on December 23, 1953.
Photo: Public Domain

The Tupolev Tu-4, a Soviet bomber used from the late 1940s to the mid-1960s, reverse-engineered from the US Boeing B-29
Photo: Public Domain

J. Robert Oppenheimer and John von Neumann (right), 1952. Oppenheimer was head of the Los Alamos Laboratory during the war and became Director of the Institute for Advanced Study in 1947. In 1955, von Neumann became a commissioner of the Atomic Energy Commission, using his position to further produce compact hydrogen bombs for intercontinental ballistic missile (ICBM) delivery.
Photo: Public Domain

General Curtis LeMay (1906–1990), U.S. Air Force Chief of Staff who, during the Cold War, advocated for World War III to begin.
Photo: Public Domain

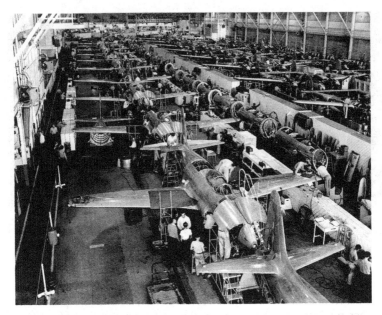

Lockheed production line
Photo: Public Domain

U.S. Air Force F-80s ("Shooting Stars") loaded with 500-pound high-explosive bombs under their wings
Photo: Public Domain

Lockheed U-2 spy plane (nicknamed "Dragon Lady") designed to obtain photographs during overflights of the Soviet Union
Photo: Public Domain

U-2 designer Kelly Johnson (left) with pilot Francis Gary Powers (right) in front of a U-2
Photo: Public Domain

Lockheed test pilot Francis Gary Powers standing with Lockheed U-2B. Powers is wearing red and white high visibility overalls over a high-altitude partial pressure suit with an MA-1 helmet.
Credit: National Air and Space Museum Archives, NASM-93-16025
Photo: Public Domain

Operation Grand Slam, May 1, 1960, flight path for Francis Gary Powers' U-2
Credit: The Central Intelligence Agency and Overhead Reconnaissance; the U-2 and Oxcart Programs, 1954–1974, declassified June 25, 2013
Photo: Public Domain

Dr. James Gilbert Baker, well-known optical physicist and astronomer, was recruited by the U.S. Army's aerial reconnaissance program to create a camera system for the U-2.
Photo: Public Domain

James R. Killian, Jr. (1904–1988) served as President Eisenhower's Special Assistant for Science and Technology from 1957 to 1959, overseeing the creation of the President's Science Advisory Committee (PSAC) after Soviet *Sputnik 1* and *Sputnik 2* were launched in October and November 1957.
Photo: Public Domain

U-2 wreckage. On May 1, 1960, American U-2 spy plane piloted by Francis Gary Powers was shot down over Soviet air space. Khrushchev condemned US spy activities.
Credit: Dwight D. Eisenhower Presidential Library, Museum & Boyhood Home

Soviet Premier Nikita Khrushchev rants with clenched fist at a press conference. He canceled the disarmament summit meeting since the United States wouldn't apologize for the American U-2 spy plane incident.
Photo: Public Domain

The Sukhoi Su-9 Soviet jet interceptor (NATO name "Fishpot") was the only interceptor in 1960 that could reach 70,000 feet. The Soviet Union sent two Su-9 interceptors after Francis Gary Powers' U-2 in Russian air space. Captain Igor Mentyukov claimed his slipstream caused the U-2 to break apart.
Photo: Public Domain

The S-75 surface-to-air missile (SAM) in transit. Its first publicized success was the shooting down of Francis Gary Powers' U-2 spy plane in 1960.
Photo: Public Domain

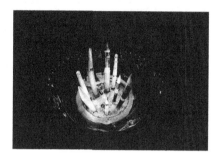

R-7 Semyorka, the world's first intercontinental ballistic missile, Moscow, Russia, developed during the Cold War. Launched on August 21, 1957, it traveled 3,700 miles. A slightly modified version launched *Sputnik* on October 4, 1957. Credit: Jupiter Images

SM-75/PGM-17A Thor missiles, the U.S. Air Force's first operational 1,500-mile, intermediate-range ballistic missile (IRBM) with thermonuclear warheads. They were 65 feet high and 8 feet in diameter. Time from UK to Moscow, 12 minutes.
Credit: National Museum of the United States Air Force

John Foster Dulles (1888–1959), U.S. Secretary of State under President Dwight D. Eisenhower from 1953 to 1959, advocated an aggressive position against communism during the Cold War. Photo: Public Domain

Effects of *Little Boy* atomic bomb on Hiroshima, Japan, on August 6, 1945
Photo: Public Domain

Soviet military intelligence Colonel Oleg Penkovsky (right) (1919–1963) on trial in Russia in 1963 for informing the United States and the United Kingdom of Soviet military secrets, including information on the locations of and weaknesses in Russia's intermediate-range ballistic missile (IRBM) installations.
Photo: Public Domain

14

June 20, 1956 – 0440 Hours
Mission 2003
Wiesbaden, Germany

Carl Overstreet felt like a stuffed sausage in the MC-3 partial pressure suit. He knew the flight would not be easy.

The least they could do is custom fit these stupid things, Overstreet thought.

It was bad enough to worry about guided missiles and the inevitable MiG-15s and MiG-17s. The tight fit in the crotch and under the arms did little to assuage his concerns. He knew damage to any part of the fragile U-2—a flying pterodactyl— would result in depressurization and instant death. He reflected on his U-2 orientation classes. He could hear the instructor. "The human respiratory system functions unassisted at altitudes up to 10,000 feet."

I'm only seven times higher. At that altitude, the barometric pressure is so low that water boils at normal body temperature and can reach minus 112 degrees Fahrenheit. After donning his headgear, Overstreet started a one-hour process where he breathed pure oxygen to dissipate any nitrogen in the bloodstream that would cause high altitude decompression sickness. The cabin pressure on the U-2 was maintained between 28,000 and 30,000 feet, and the MC-3 suit automatically pressurized to 3 psi. He went over the details of the S and X-band ELINT receivers located in the nose to collect ground-controlled intercept and air defense signals.[71]

Overstreet was strapped into his airplane at approximately 0600 hours. Shortly thereafter, Bissell (six hours behind Wiesbaden local time) sent the go signal. The control device from the

Wiesbaden control tower flashed from red to green. The U-2 rolled down the runway, gained speed to approximately 90 knots, and began a steep initial climb to 25,000 feet. It took a heading of 280 degrees toward Belgium. Overstreet turned back to overfly Wiesbaden before crossing into hostile territory where the borders of East and West Germany and Czechoslovakia converged.[72]

Within forty minutes, the plane was at 60,000 feet. Overstreet initiated the cruise climb and engaged the autopilot to hold a constant speed. The plane flew over Prague before entering Poland. The Agency and Air Force wanted to see if the Poles, East Germans, and Czechs coordinated their tracking—if they were tracking at all. The U-2 continued to Bydgoszcz before turning southeast to Warsaw and Lublin. Overstreet was momentarily confused but righted himself and turned back to Krakow and Wroclaw while maintaining an altitude in excess of 69,000 feet.

He overflew Prague again, but this time on a southwest path, continuing into NATO territory all the way to the Rhine and the Franco-German border before returning to Wiesbaden. The next day, Bissell, Edwin, Land, and TCP Chairman James Killian went to the White House to meet with Eisenhower's military aide, Colonel Andrew Goodpaster.[73] The President was in the hospital with a stomach issue.

While in the hospital, Eisenhower had tentatively authorized a ten-day window of overflights in July. Bissell asked if he meant ten consecutive days or ten days of good weather. Colonel Goodpaster made sure Bissell understood the approval was for ten straight days. German Chancellor Konrad Adenauer didn't know the Eastern Bloc countries had been overflown, nor did he know that the U-2s were planning to scope out Russia from Wiesbaden. Eisenhower made it clear that any overflights of the Soviet Union were contingent on Bissell's obtaining the Chancellor's permission. Eisenhower also spiked any Soviet Union overflights while U.S. Air Force Chief of Staff Nathan

Twining and his entourage were being entertained at the Tushino Airfield near Moscow. General Twining was not scheduled to leave Moscow until July 1.

Bissell had to deal with Chancellor Adenauer first. He and CIA Deputy Director Charles Pearre Cabell promptly hopped a flight to Germany. When presented with the concept, Chancellor Adenauer said, "This is a wonderful idea. It's just what ought to be done."

∞

June 22, 1956 – 1008 Hours
CIA Photo Intelligence Division
aka HTAUTOMAT
1015 5th Street Northwest
Washington, DC

The new Photo Intelligence Division (PID) lab was going to be located between the Steuart Insurance Agency and an automobile parts department store. From what Bissell had been told, the ancient and completely irrelevant directory in the lobby provided a nice touch to the inauspicious nature of the milieu. Bissell and Caleb had just finished viewing the photos from the June 20 overflight before they took off to meet the Chancellor.[74] Although James Baker's primary camera was not quite ready, everyone was generally pleased with the quality of the photos from the A-2 camera.

They drove past the PID lab. The neighborhood and the building looked perfect to Bissell because they would not draw any attention to the top-secret activities. Bissell noticed a sign in the shop window. He parked and wandered over to investigate. Within seconds, he was on a pay phone.

The unfortunate agent who fielded the call got an earful.

"There's a sign, Carson."

"Sir?"

"A sign in the window . . . in the window of a top-secret photo lab."

"And that's a problem?"

"The damn thing reads, 'Rented to the CIA.' Do you think that's a problem, Carson?"

The sign disappeared within the hour. To Bissell's relief, Director Dulles never knew about it.

15

June 30, 1956 – 1759 Hours
House of the Soviet Army
Moscow, Russia

Defense Minister General Georgy Zhukov, Chief Air Marshal Pavel Zhigarev, and Premier Nikita Khrushchev took the leaders of the US, British, and French delegations to a park at the House of the Soviet Army. The assembled sat at a picnic table. They'd just viewed an impressive Soviet air show.

Khrushchev stood and proposed a toast "in defense of peace." It was his typical, long-winded banter worthy of a stump speech. He turned to General Twining and said, "Today we showed you our aircraft, but would you like to have a look at our missiles?"

"Yes, I would," General Twining responded.

Khrushchev chuckled—like a teenager who had played a prank. "Well, we will not show them to you. First show us your aircraft, and stop sending intruders into our airspace. We will shoot down uninvited guests. We will get all your Canberras. They are flying coffins."

Silence weighed heavily on the group. Khrushchev noticed a US military attaché pouring the contents of his glass under a bush. Khrushchev, face flushed, looked at Ambassador Charles Bolin. "I am speaking about peace and friendship, and what does your military attaché do? He empties his glass in the bushes."[75]

Bolin clenched his jaw and goaded the young man into drinking a hefty penalty toast to Soviet and American friendship—and then another. The young attaché could not hold his third toast and was soon face-first in the bushes where the contents of his stomach joined his discarded drink.

Abandoning his traditional role as a bully, Khrushchev went over to see if the attaché needed medical help. Twining made a mental note of the uncharacteristic act of kindness. When he returned to Washington, Twining filed a report in which he repeated the Russians' belief about the Canberra overflights. Bissell and Dulles were pleased there had been no mention of the Americans' newest entry in the aerial spy wars.

∽

July 2, 1956 – 0600 Hours
Missions 2009/2010
Wiesbaden Air Base, West Germany

Jake Kratt took off approximately fifteen minutes before Glenn Dunaway. Kratt flew south across Austria and then into Hungary. When he passed over Budapest, he turned south and flew along the Yugoslavian border. He crossed Bulgaria to the Black Sea and then headed back to Wiesbaden. Unfortunately, Kratt's A-2 camera was damaged, and the Agency was unable to recover any usable photographs.

Dunaway headed north over East Germany, went on to southern Poland, and then flew over eastern Czechoslovakia to Hungary and Romania before turning around at the Black Sea and returning to Wiesbaden.[76] Each flight took seven hours. Bissell, who had returned to Washington later that day, met with DDCI Cabell in the Oval Office with Eisenhower. The President was generally upbeat about the project and found the overflight photographs from Dunaway's flight "very interesting, very positive." Eisenhower's main concern had to do with whether the flights were constantly and accurately tracked.

"Bissell," Eisenhower asked, "what do you have for me concerning the June 20 flight? Was it detected and tracked by ground control radar and communication intercepts? Were any planes scrambled? Were there other air defense efforts?"

"Sir, the air defense systems in the Eastern Bloc countries operate either the P-3 Dumbo or the P-20 Barlock radar. The ELINT in the nose of the U-2 on the June 20 flight listened for radar activity in the S and X band. The System 1 tape revealed that token and other radar signals were constantly received during the flight. But the signal received by the radar operator would have indicated that the U-2 was traveling at 42,000 feet in altitude, and that was incorrect. So although the plane was tracked, it was not accurate. The plane is too high for the systems. At least that's my assessment."

"If there is any information concerning tracking this morning's flights, I want it immediately," Eisenhower ordered.

"Mr. President, we have four aircraft. We can perform two flights per day. We are anxious to get started."

"Do not miss my point, Bissell. I want constant updates about whether we are being tracked."

"Understood, Mr. President. As soon as I know, you will know."

Although Eisenhower still had his misgivings (and might have even revoked permission for the ten days of overflights if he had read General Twining's brief from the Soviet air show), the CIA continued the missions. Between July 4 and July 10, 1956, the CIA made five flights, each spending more than eight hours over Soviet airspace.[77]

∞

July 4, 1956 – 0600 Hours
Mission 2013
Wiesbaden Air Base, West Germany

Hervey Stockman passed over Poznan, Poland, between 69,000 and 70,000 feet. He maintained his cruising speed as he proceeded over Grodno in Byelorussia. His mission included photographing various bomber bases around Minsk, but the primary purpose was to provide intelligence on the submarine pens and bomber bases at Leningrad.

After finishing off the bomber bases near Minsk, he zigzagged his way up to Leningrad. He kept his speed between the stall line (430 mph) and 442 mph. After covering all his targets near Leningrad, he turned west and photographed more bomber bases in the Baltic. When he returned to Wiesbaden, he'd been aloft eight hours and forty-five minutes. In the debriefing room, Stockman mentioned that he had made good use of the view sight, a downward-looking periscope. He'd seen numerous Soviet fighters below him. Although they did not pose any threat—and he wasn't sure they'd ever spotted him— Stockman could tell they were searching (in vain) for a target that the ground controllers had identified.[78]

☙

July 5, 1956 – 0600 Hours
Mission 2014
Wiesbaden Air Base, West Germany

Carmine Vito's primary task was a little different from Stockman's. He was to search for Bison bombers. Even prior to the article in *Aviation Week*, a February 15, 1954, story speculated that the Myasishchev M-4 could carry nuclear bombs to the United States. No one ever asked whether it could make a round trip. The gullible US public was left to presuppose the bombers would cruise back to the Motherland.

They could not.

At the air show, the Russians had circulated their ten active M-4s and left the CIA to conclude there would be an entire armada of more than 800 Soviet "intercontinental bombers" by 1960.[79]

Vito's flight took him over Warsaw, Poland, and into the Soviet Union where he turned northeasterly to pass over some

124

airfields near Minsk. He followed the railroad tracks all the way to Moscow and went east for another 200 miles before turning and flying over Kaliningrad on his return to Wiesbaden. He reported the same numerous attempts at interception by MiG-15 and MiG-17 aircraft. They employed a yo-yo type of flight path in an attempt to gain altitude. They dove and then yanked into a sharp climb only to belly flop more than 3 miles below the U-2.

Vito's flight was successful and produced valuable targeting information for both the Navy and the Air Force. But he did not find any bombers. When the System 1 radar tape was read back at the Agency's facilities, analysts noted that Vito's U-2 was detected by an early warning radar system. It presented a signal they hadn't previously seen.

The U-2 was more than 150 miles east of Smolensk when the radar signal bounced off the plane, but no MiGs were scrambled. The Agency would later identify the unknown radar as the P-12 Yenisei (NATO's reporting name, "Spoon Rest A"). The P-12 was an improvement. It offered a greater range and increased frequency agility. It returned to four preset frequencies automatically and provided automatic frequency fine-tuning. It was the first Russian radar to use the coherent cancellation moving target indicator (MTI). The P-12 employed a single multi-stage antenna for both transmission and reception. The antenna was composed of twelve Yagi antennas mounted in sets of six, one set above the other. The antenna was rotated mechanically at a speed of 10 rpm. The elevation was determined by using a goniometer that utilized the phase comparison between the upper and lower antenna sets. The P-12 used two indicators, a plan position indicator in addition to an E-scope to show altitude. The P-12 could integrate tracking information from an additional radar with both sets of information appearing on the plan position indicator. It started tracking at a distance of 140 miles and could track up to an altitude of 80,000 feet. The apparatus was much more sophisticated than anything the CIA thought the Russians had developed.[80]

⚘

July 5, 1956 – 1000 Hours
CIA Headquarters
Langley, Virginia

DCI Allen Dulles strolled past Richard Bissell's office like a man strolling around a lake on a Sunday afternoon. "Did we put any birds in the air over the holiday?"

Bissell answered without looking up from his newspaper. "Yes. We sent Stockman out yesterday. Vito just returned from his flight about an hour ago."

No contact over the day off meant there had not been any emergencies. Still, Dulles was curious about the details on the flights. "Any reports on intercept attempts I should be aware of?" he asked.

Bissell looked up. "Unfortunately, the news on that front isn't very positive."

Dulles slid into a seat. "Interesting—and curious. What could be so bad? After all, we won't have the photos or the System 1 readout for several days."

Bissell knew Dulles wouldn't like what he was going to say. "Well, when both pilots tell me the photos should be of very good quality with only one drawback—"[81]

"Which is?"

"Obstruction or interference from a significant number of fighter planes attempting intercepts."

"Not going to make Ike very happy," Dulles said.

"No, it's not," Bissell said. "We're going to get wrung out about telling him how lucky the Soviet radar would have to be to detect a plane at 70,000 feet, much less track it."

126

Dulles didn't appear upset. "I'm sure he won't like it, but I need more details on the flights. What areas did they cover, and did they find any bombers?"

Bissell shook his head. "We won't know for a few days, but Stockman went north and Vito east."

"How far north and how far east?"

"Vito went a couple hundred kilometers past Moscow, and Stockman went about eighty north of Leningrad."

Dulles winced with his next utterance. "Tell me Vito knew about the SAMs surrounding Moscow. Tell me he stayed more than a hundred miles north or south."

The Adam's apple on Bissell's neck bobbed. "Not exactly."

"How much not exactly?"

"Flew right over it."

"Son of a b——." Dulles returned to his seat, which had flown back about two feet when he leaped up. "First time out and that jet jockey tools over Moscow?"

Bissell scratched his forehead. "Well, Vito's flight was on the second day, if that matters."

"You know it doesn't," Dulles said. "Let me guess. Stockman flew directly over Leningrad?"

Bissell nodded like a schoolboy reprimanded in Sunday school. "My call, sir," he said. "I figured the defenses over those two cities are only going to get better. I decided we needed to get a jump."

Dulles smoothed his tie and stood. "Bissell, you are a very brave man."

Bissell smiled.

"But you might be the dumbest sumofabitch in Washington."

⁓

Bissell still had five days of Eisenhower's initial overflight authorization. Both Dulles and Bissell knew that if Eisenhower learned about all the intercept attempts, the permission would evaporate. Colonel Goodpaster called both men on July 6 and told them the operation should be suspended immediately if they had any information or warning that the flights had been detected or tracked. One radar readout from the July 4th and July 5th flights indicated that although numerous intercepts had been attempted, the Soviet radar was softest around Moscow and Leningrad. Since no Soviet fighter had managed to get within three miles of the U-2, when the weather cooperated on July 9 and 10, Bissell sent out three missions. The most important of the three turned out to be Mission 2020.

On July 9, 1956, Marty Knutson overflew the Engels Airfield in the Saratov Oblast approximately 723 kilometers southeast of Moscow. There he photographed thirty M-4 Myasishchev bombers. By this time, the Agency was beginning to suspect that Khrushchev was lying. Despite wild CIA and Air Force estimates to the contrary, the Russians only had thirty Bison bombers.

The other two flights, though ambitious and a little aggressive, turned up no added information on modern bombers.

16

July 10, 1956 – 1547 Hours
U.S. Embassy, Moscow

"Ambassador Bohlen, I have a message from the Kremlin, and I believe you may want to read it right away," the ambassador's stenographer said.

Charles Bohlen knew whatever he'd been handed would not be good news. He scanned the missive. "It seems our Soviet friends have taken umbrage to some intelligence-gathering techniques," he said. "They think we have something to do with high-altitude bombers. He dictated this memo to Washington."

According to precisely verified data, on July 4 of this year, at 8:18 a.m. Moscow Time, a twin-engined medium bomber of the United States Air Force appeared from the American Zone of Occupation in Western Germany and flew over the territory of the German Democratic Republic, entering the air space of the Soviet Union from the direction of the Polish People's Republic at 9:35 in the area of Grodno. The aircraft which violated the air space of the Soviet Union flew on the route Minsk, Vilnyus, Kaunas and Kaliningrad, penetrating territory of the Soviet Union to the depth of 320 kilometers and remaining over such territory for one hour and 32 minutes.

He paused to ensure the stenographer was current.

On July 5 of this year, at 7:41 Moscow Time, a twin-engine medium bomber of the United States Air Force, coming from the American Zone of Occupation in Western Germany, flew over the territory of the German Democratic Republic, and at 8:54 penetrated the air space of the Soviet Union in the area of Brest, coming from the direction of the Polish People's Republic. The aircraft violating the air frontier of the Soviet Union flew along the route Brest, Pinsk Baranovichi, Kaunas, and Kaliningrad, having penetrated Soviet territory to a depth of 150 kilometers and having remained one hour and 20 minutes over such territory.

While the stenographer tried not to show any reaction, Bohlen saw her wince. "I know," he said. "This isn't good."

She straightened her glasses and sat with pencil poised over the pad.

He continued dictating the memo.

The same day another twin-engine bomber of the United States Air Force invaded the air space of the Soviet Union and penetrated to a significant depth over Soviet territory. On July 9 there took place new flights of United States aircraft into the Soviet air space.

He looked up. "That is all. Send it top secret and urgent."[82]

The stenographer left.

Bohlen hurled a coffee cup against the far wall of his office. "For the love of God, can someone please tell me what the hell is going on around here?"

∞

A little earlier, another coffee cup had met a similar fate against Khrushchev's office wall in the Kremlin. The Premier's chubby face turned a deep scarlet while he unleashed a string of invectives. On July 4 he had been at the U.S. Embassy wishing the United States a happy 180th birthday. It had been all smiles and toasts. All the while he was receiving secret reports about the overflights.

He had not let on to Ambassador Bohlen or anyone else at the Embassy, but beneath his jovial exterior, he was seething. He was not upset about the attempt to gather intelligence since he was no virgin in the world of international intrigue. His wrath came from his impotence to stop it. He had summoned his best engineers and finest military leaders in hopes of finding a quick solution.

The forecast was not promising.

∽

July 17, 1956 – 0816 Hours
Senate Building, the Kremlin

Artem Mikoyan, Andrei Tupolev, Sergey Ilyushin, Pyotr Dmitrievich Grushin, Pavel Osipovich Sukhoi, and other experts on the design of interceptors and anti-aircraft missiles met with Khrushchev on July 17, 1956. Khrushchev's main concern was whether the plane they'd been powerless to stop could carry a nuclear bomb. Tupolev had not seen a silhouette of the plane and had no data other than the altitude, the speed, and (to some extent) the duration of its flight.

"We are dealing with a craft built at the very edge of what is possible for altitude and speed," Tupolev stated. "In such a case, carrying capacity is calculated in grams. Even the slightest excess weight would result in a substantial loss of altitude. I therefore conclude that it could not carry any substantial payload."

The plane reminded Tupolev of his monoplane, the ANT-25, from the pre-Great War. It was built specifically to set flight records. It made a sensational, nonstop flight over the North Pole from Moscow to the United States in the 1930s. It had only a single engine, so he adamantly asserted it could not have been a twin-engine Canberra. Mikoyan and Sukhoi opined that it would take three to four years of intense work to design a plane to bring down the intruder.

Khrushchev made no attempt to hide his frustration. "The Americans are not only counting our bombers and missiles, but they are also mapping flight paths to avoid our radar installations. They are seeking to destroy any ability to answer their first strike. If you do not have a solution to this problem within the next year, it will be fine . . ."

No one moved. They knew the next line.

". . . because you will all be dead."

131

No one asked if Khrushchev meant it would be by firing squad or in a nuclear holocaust. No one wanted to be the first person to break the oppressive silence. The Premier called on the Chief Marshal of his Air Defense Ministry.

"Comrade Biryuzov, what are you going to do to stop the American spy planes?"

Sergey Biryuzov took a full fifteen seconds before his rich baritone voice echoed off the walls. "We shoot them down." Then he slumped into his seat and looked at the ceiling.

Marshal Zhukov, the Minister of Defense, rose before a bemused or perhaps stunned Khrushchev could launch a verbal attack. "First, Secretary Khrushchev, I am sure Chief Marshal Biryuzov would like to share with us his plans for putting the American pilots in a flying coffin."

This time, Biryuzov used two words instead of four. "Alexander Raspletin."

Grushin stood. "The Chief Marshal is referring to our new C-75 Dvina surface-to-air missile system designed by Raspletin, which will be deployed very soon. When an American pilot flies over a C-75 battery, he will be shot down."

Khrushchev squinted. "We have Systema C-25 in two rings around Moscow. Why wasn't the American spy eliminated?"

Grushin swallowed. No one ever knew the result of telling the truth to the pugnacious Soviet leader. "As you know, we have an outer ring 80 kilometers from Moscow. It features thirty-four Systema-25 sites. An installation 45 kilometers outside of Moscow has twenty-two. Each site contains up to sixty radar-guided missiles. The S band VNIIRT R-113 or our P-12 Yensi can acquire a Target 200 to 300 kilometers away from the missile battery. When the target gets closer, the long-range acquisition system transfers the target to our B-200 radar system with a range of 150 kilometers. There are two narrow beams, one to track the target and one to command the missile."

Khrushchev made no move to interrupt.

Grushin continued. "Each of our Systema-25 regiments can engage up to twenty targets simultaneously—three missiles per intruder. In theory, we can shoot down more than 1,000 American bombers at the same time. The Separate Army for Special Purposes, a division of our Soviet Air Defense Forces (PVO Strany) under the command of General Colonel Kazakov, mans our Systema-25 batteries. When the American plane was first acquired, it was at an altitude of 73,000 feet. They ignored it because a plane cannot fly that high, and an attack would not be carried out by a single plane. The men of the Army for Special Purposes are highly trained. They did not want to waste a good missile."

"Why would the missile have been wasted?" Krushchev asked.

"The missile," Grushin responded, "is a single-stage liquid propellant with a 200 to 320 kilogram high-explosive warhead. The missile is slow to lift off, so it is not effective against bombers with supersonic speeds."

"But the American plane was well below supersonic speed. So where's the problem?" Khrushchev barked.

"The altitude, sir," Grushin answered. "The C-25 can reach a speed of Mach 2.5 but will not go above 18,000 meters. Since the Americans are developing at least one supersonic bomber (the B-58) and the B-52 is likely to attack at altitudes below 900 meters, the Systema-25 is obsolete. As Chief Marshal Biryuzov suggested, the C-75, which will be deployed within one year, is our best system to bring down the high-altitude American spy plane."

Khrushchev raised one finger, an indication for Grushin to stop. "Why is the C-75 so superior?"

Grushin sounded like a university professor explaining gravity to a cocker spaniel. "Whereas the C-25 is stationary, the C-75 is mobile and can be launched from an SM-90 trainable, single rail launcher carried by a semitrailer. The C-25 is a single stage propelled by a hypergolic liquids mix. The C-75 is a two-stage missile with a solid propellant utilized for the first stage while a similar hypergolic liquid mix powers the new Isayev S2.711 second-stage engine. This missile will accelerate off the launchpad and reach a top speed of Mach 3.5 and an altitude of over 25,000 meters while carrying a highly explosive warhead of 195 kilograms with a lethal blast radius of up to 244 meters at a 25,000-meter altitude. It is also effective against low-altitude bombing runs where the target is higher than 100 meters."

He waited. Khrushchev nodded.

"The guidance system is similar to the C-25. There is no high learning curve for the Army for Special Purposes. The acquisition radar is the same as currently used by the C-25 regiments. Retargeting radar is a variant of the B–200. It is called the RSNA/SNR-75, or Fan Song as NATO refers to it. Each missile battery will contain six launchers and one nearby SNR-75 radar system that has three dishes, two of which can be carried on a single trailer. Once the tracking information is transferred to the SNR-75, the entire antenna package orients in the direction of the target and initiates angle and range tracking with an analog computer. The computer steers the missile toward the target. Defense Minister Zhukov has recently chosen the C-75 over the Obiekt 400 due to its lower cost, its lower learning curve, and its availability at a much earlier date."

Khrushchev grunted. "So when will we shoot down the American spy?"

"Soon," Grushin said. "It won't be long before he makes a mistake and flies over one of our C-75 batteries."

17

July 11, 1956 – 0917 Hours
The White House
Washington, DC

Eisenhower had been suspicious of the silence about the overflights from Moscow. Perhaps they had not seen the planes. Or perhaps they were too proud to admit their powerlessness in the face of superior technology.

Then he received the System 1 ELINT data. Dulles and Bissell had been completely wrong about the archaic state of the Soviet radar system.

Eisenhower was not a happy man. He had not led the Allies to victory in World War II by underestimating the enemy. Another thought plagued him. *If they were wrong about the radar, chances are they are mistaken about the Soviets' inability to shoot down one of our boys.*

He wasn't entirely sure that Dulles and Bissell appreciated the gravity of the situation should the Soviets bring down a U-2 in Russian territory. He knew his old friend Marshal Zhukov, the Soviet equivalent of the Secretary of Defense and a brilliant military tactician, would conclude that the U-2 overflights were mapping targets in preparation for a US preventative first strike.

It was time to educate the CIA about world politics before the Soviets got jumpy and kick-started a general war, a conflict in which they currently held a significant advantage.

Eisenhower picked up the phone. "Colonel Pasteur, get Dulles and Bissell over here at one o'clock. No excused absences."

∞

Caleb Young was in Richard Bissell's office. Dulles shook his hand and then looked at Bissell.

"Richard, the President wants to see us at 1300 hours. Dr. Young, you were not summoned, but I want you to come along. I believe you agreed with Colonel Leghorn about the inability of Soviet radar to operate at an altitude above 60,000 feet."

Caleb was used to Dulles's habit of shooting from the hip.

"Director Dulles, I haven't any idea what you're talking about. You must have me confused with one of the other scientists. I never professed to be an expert on Russian radar."

Dulles laughed. "Be that as it may, you're coming. The encounter with the President will not be a party in the Rose Garden. It might not be fun, but it will be memorable. Not everyone can say they got an ass-chewing from a former five-star general."

"I'll meet you there," Caleb said.

Bissell shook his head. "Nice try, Young. You're driving all of us."

∞

July 11, 1956 – 1300 Hours
Oval Office, the White House
Washington, DC

There were no cowards in the room, but every man trembled internally under the President's focused stare.

"When were you fellows going to tell me about the scrambled MiGs?" Eisenhower asked but didn't wait for an answer. "I hear tell they were so thick the U-2 boys couldn't see the ground."

When it became obvious that no one wanted to speak, Dulles took the lead. "Mr. President, we didn't think the situation presented any imminent danger to our pilots, and the information gathered during the five overflights of the Soviet

Union provided significant intelligence on the Soviets' long-range bomber capabilities."

"I've seen the reports," Eisenhower said, "but I have also been hearing from Ambassador Zarubin. They aren't happy. Any more incursions will result in Russian overflights of US installations . . . and you know . . . we . . . cannot . . . have . . . that."

Dulles paused a beat. He didn't want to sound like a door-to-door Electrolux salesman.

"Sir," Dulles said, "the Soviets don't have a clue about what type of plane we have. And they completely missed two of our missions—the ones over Leningrad and Moscow. They cannot consistently track the U-2 long enough to fire at it. We believe we have located their entire long-range bomber fleet, fewer than 100 planes. Since we do not believe the Bison can make a round-trip flight to the United States, they have no more than seventy."

Dulles took a breath and decided to move on. "Along with the military intelligence services, we will soon have over 100 new targets based on the photographs we have. We are preparing to overfly Kapustin Yar and Tyuratam to determine where the Soviets are in missile development."

Eisenhower's rage was palpable, but his tone remained measured. "General Twining just got back from the Russian air show. He had a rather unpleasant stroll in the park with Khrushchev and Marshal Zhigarev."

Bissell screwed up his courage. "The U-2s have yet to go over the missile sites. We need the information so we can take them out within the first two hours of any hostilities. Otherwise, our European allies will suffer unfathomable consequences."

The comment only enraged the President further. "Stop trying to manage me, and start *thinking*. If they know we can take out their sites, they will be less confident. That makes trigger fingers twitchy, gentlemen. They need the comfort blanket of their deterrent. What happens next?"

No one answered.

"Holy Mother of God," Eisenhower continued. "You people are supposed to be the best analysts in the business. Here's what happens. Russia gets nervous. The Joint Chiefs catch wind of it and begin planning a first strike. We have more security holes than Carter has little pills, so the Russians will probably know about our plans before I've gotten past the first page. Once they figure they have nothing to lose, it will be Katy bar the door. If they are sure they are going to be attacked, they won't give two hoots in hell about starting something on their own."

He looked at each man for a full five seconds each.

"Do you get that?"

Eisenhower understood Khrushchev's blustering nature and was willing to live with it. He knew this First Secretary of the Communist Party was trying to soothe the military as he drew down defense spending to goose the standard of living.

"Gentlemen, I'm not happy. I think you can tell. When I say I want to know, what does that mean? Allen?"

At least Allen Dulles was man enough to look his boss in the eye. "It means you want to know."

"When do I want to know it?"

"Soon."

"As in immediately. The second you know something, I know it. Are we clear?"

"Yes, sir."

"You don't filter anything. Got it?"

"Yes, sir."

Eisenhower took a breath. His face returned to its normal color. "Now we are going to have to live with the Soviets on this planet whether we like it or not. For the most part, I judge Khrushchev as a very significant step in the right direction. He's not Stalin, and he's walking a very fine line between the right-wing hardliners and his political ambitions to achieve detente with the West. Our overflights to date have revealed that we do not face a significant threat of a sneak attack by the Soviets. Correct?"

Dulles nodded.

"Good. Now we cannot let our guard down, but it appears that further overflights are not warranted at this time. They will do more harm than good. They may even truncate Khrushchev's attempts to de-Stalinize the Soviet Union. So, and let me be clear, we are suspending any overflights until we modify the plane and until we can disguise its present signature. The Soviets must believe it is a blip or something other than a reconnaissance plane. We have totally underestimated their radar capabilities, and we don't want to do the same with their SAMs. If we do, we'll have a downed plane, a dead pilot, and an international incident. At best we will be characterized as flaunting international law. At worst, we will provoke a series of responses destined to raise everyone's blood pressure and pose a dire threat to human life."

Again, the stares.

"One more time. All overflights of Soviet territory are canceled until I okay them personally. That's all for now."

Everyone stood.

Eisenhower looked at Caleb. "Dr. Young, I'd like you to stay for a while. I've got some questions."

Eisenhower shook Dulles's hand. "You'll need another chauffeur. And don't use Bissell. I'm pretty sure he doesn't even have a driver's license."

∽

"Dr. Young, I've noticed your absence from the NSC briefings," Eisenhower began.

Caleb wasn't sure where the President was headed or why he had asked him to stay. He'd always been very complimentary, and Caleb knew Ike respected his intellect and skill. He had also mentioned Caleb's discussions on the Princeton campus with Einstein about dropping the bomb on Japan.

"I'm sure Dr. Killian has kept you up to date on the development of smaller thermal nuclear warheads that can be delivered with intercontinental ballistic missiles," Caleb said. "I've been engaged in a summer study on the feasibility of submarine-launched ballistic missiles (SLBMs) with nuclear warheads at Woods Hole, Massachusetts."

"Project Nobska," Eisenhower said.

Caleb couldn't hide his surprise. *He is very well-informed,* Caleb thought.

"Yes, sir," Caleb responded. "The Navy is well on its way to developing a sub-based missile that can be launched without surfacing." Caleb paused and then decided that full disclosure was best. "When that happens, you will have your hands full."

"Say more," he said.

"Once the Navy can fire nukes from under water, the Jack Tars will be in here asking you to relegate the Air Force to second-fiddle status as our major nuclear deterrent force."

Eisenhower's brow furrowed. "Doctor Young, I have to make tough decisions in this room. I asked you to stay behind because I know you are not burdened by social protocols."

"Pardon?"

"You call a spade a spade. You don't candy-coat things. I need direct answers."

"I'll take that as a compliment, sir."

"As intended." Eisenhower took a sip of water. "Neither Einstein nor I approved of Truman's decision to drop the atomic bomb on Japan. I want your best take on what your former mentor would think about the current state of world affairs. I made a lot of tough calls during the war, but the ones I am facing could tally more casualties in one day than in all the months from Pearl Harbor to V-J Day combined."

Caleb took a moment to collect his thoughts before responding. "Mr. President, my philosophy and Dr. Einstein's are very different when it comes to the nature of man and what type of structure is or is not necessary to create a civilized society. I do not believe that the Soviets feel they can conquer us militarily. They believe capitalism is inherently flawed and will collapse under its own weight. They believe that communism will eventually rule the world based on their understanding of the nature of man. So I do not believe we are threatened militarily as long as we are strong enough to defend ourselves."

"Go on."

"Recent history indicates they will push until we push back. But I believe communism will implode before capitalism as predicted by Plato in *The Republic*. Over the last couple of years, there has been strong evidence of its eventual collapse. Consider what happened in Poland in the summer of 1955. They held the Fifth World Festival of Youth and Students, an event attended by hundreds of thousands of Polish spectators in Warsaw. Local Poles came to realize that for the last ten years, the Soviet anti-Western rhetoric has been false. After the death of the First Secretary of the Polish United Workers Party Bolesław Beirut in Moscow earlier this year, the Poznan protests took place, resulting in the deaths of around eighty people. But the workers achieved a 50 percent pay raise and more political independence from Moscow.

"Just a couple years before that, we had the East Berlin uprising. I believe we are beginning to see cracks in the Iron Curtain. Your decision to suspend any future overflights until the situation changes is sagacious. No one has shared the information about the U-2 with the Soviet public. If the overflights become so pervasive that Khrushchev cannot save face, he will be ousted, and a more militaristic regime will take charge in the Kremlin. If you continue the overflights, they could reveal military weakness, and then you could face more political pressure to roll back the Iron Curtain like Senator Taft promised to do in the primaries four years ago. And you will be pushed by some in our military to preempt while we have an overwhelming advantage. If the situation changes and the Soviets look like they have a significant missile advantage, the flights can continue. For now, I think we can safely assume there is no credible threat of a first Soviet strike by their bombers."

Caleb could only imagine how General Patton must have felt under Eisenhower's intense gaze.

"Why do you work on weapons that have the capability of killing millions?" Eisenhower asked.

Caleb didn't flinch. "Because with you in this office, I know the person who possesses the power over them will use them for peace and not war."

Ike never said what he thought of Caleb's speculations. He thanked Caleb, and Caleb left.

Three months later, unrest behind the Iron Curtain reared its head in Hungary.

⚬⚭⚬

Bissell and Dulles exited the White House. Dulles's brows nearly met in the middle of his frowning face. "Looks like you need to get with Kelly and see if the design can be modified to change the radar signature. Then we'll test it."

"I'm sure Kelly will have some ideas," Bissell said, "but we don't want anything that might change the plane's performance. The results are great so far. The Soviet MiGs are more than 2 miles below the U-2s, and the missile sites need so much lead time that it's doubtful they can coordinate radar sighting and launch preparation before the plane's gone."

Dulles got in the car. They'd summoned a driver. "You know, Ike's ass is in a sling if we screw this up. System One ELINT signals in some areas indicate the Soviets have increased the density of their radar POPs per sector. They might be able to track long enough to coordinate the radar image and make in-flight adjustments for their SAMs. We believe they are using the S-band VNIIRT R-13 Kama radar. It can acquire up to a range of 190 miles. It's doubtful that the B-200 Yo-Yo targeting radar can be coordinated with the Kama, according to our guys."

Bissell nodded while he lit a cigarette. "Well, let's see what we can do because this is too promising to stop now. We have to find out about their missiles, even if it upsets Ike."

∞

Back at Lockheed, Kelly Johnson and his engineering team looked at the problem and determined they could implement some adjustments, but nothing was going to make the U-2 invisible. Only three of the engineers on the project had any experience with radar and the accompanying guidance systems for SAMs. They started Project Rainbow, and even though they involved Edward Purcell, a Nobel Prize winner in Physics from Harvard, and Frank Rodgers from MIT, they were unable to stop radar from tracking the U-2. Regardless, Eisenhower used the U-2 to spy on the British and the French during the Suez Crisis in the late summer and fall of 1956.

18

August 29, 1956
Wiesbaden Air Base, West Germany

President Gamal Abdel Nasser of Egypt had threatened to close the Suez Canal in the summer of 1956, a move promising significant damage to English and French economies. Along with Israel, England and France prepared for a surprise invasion of Egypt. Secretary of State John Foster Dulles importuned Eisenhower to commence flights over staging areas for the invasion in order to discourage the combatants.

The mission involved two U-2s, eight hours each. They would land at Incirlik Air Base in western Turkey, retrace their routes the next day, and return to Wiesbaden. There was an unspoken US policy to nudge England and France from their dominant positions of influence in the Middle East before the Soviet Union could convince Syria and Egypt that their interests were better served by forming an alliance with the Warsaw Pact. There were plans for future excursions in September if the Suez conflict heated up.

Although the planes at Wiesbaden were seldom out of their hangars, for reasons unknown, the aircrew handling some of the Suez missions left a few of the planes on the runway, which was normally not a problem. But Wiesbaden was located near a busy highway, which prompted curious onlookers to wonder, "What's with the planes with the long, big, floppy wings?"

Dulles was considerably less than pleased when he heard about the sightseers. He summoned Bissell. "What the hell? We've busted our humps to hide this plane, and then a couple of yahoos from Nebraska or some other godforsaken place take a beer break and park it in the driveway. Why didn't they just take out a newspaper ad: 'Super-Secret Spy Plane on Exhibit from Noon 'til Two'?"

"All the planes should be in Giebelstadt within the next week," Bissell said.

"That's not a solution, and you know it," Dulles said. "They've already seen the 'man behind the curtain.' What did we say to them?"

"Who?"

Dulles lost his legendary cool, cursed, and snapped a pencil in half. "The people who were staring at the elephant through the fence! Have you been paying attention?"

"Sorry, Allen," Bissell said.

"Right now, I am 'Director,'" Dulles said.

Bissell had visions of secret CIA locations where people went to disappear. "Uh . . . we told them the planes were relics from World War II. The wings were drooping because they are old."

"So we pissed in their ears and told them it was raining," Dulles said. Another pencil came to an untimely demise. "Unbelievable!"

"I don't know if they believed it or not, Mr. Director. The second detachment is set up at Incirlik. It will handle most of the rest of the Middle East flights. I think that by the end of the year we'll be out of Germany completely. What do you think the British and French are up to over in the Middle East?"

Dulles knew a misdirection when he saw one, but pursuing the matter would not solve anything. "On July 26, Nasser announced that the Suez Canal belongs to Egypt. My guess is that sooner rather than later, Egypt's going to have some uninvited, heavily armed guests. We've seen quite a buildup of military forces by the British and French in Malta, Cypress, and the Mediterranean."

"Well, I'm not surprised," said Bissell. "When Congress refused to allocate money for the Aswan Dam project, it gave the Russians a wide-open invitation to solidify their relationship with Egypt. So what's Eisenhower's take on all this?"

Dulles bit his lip. "Ike has warned them that they are in the process of violating the Tripartite Declaration of 1950 in which we agreed with Britain and France to take action to prevent any violation of the 1949 Armistice Line, the so-called Green Line, separating Israel from its Arab neighbors."[83]

"Israel is involved?"

"In the Middle East? What are the chances?" Dulles said with a large dose of sarcasm. He didn't smile. "Yes, the NSA has intercepts, and our Embassy in Paris found out that between October 22nd and 24th, British Prime Minister Eden sent Defense Minister Selwyn Lloyd to Sèvres. David Ben-Gurion, Prime Minister of Israel; Moshe Dayan, Israel's military leader; and Shimon Peres met with Guy Mollet, Christian Pineau, and Maurice Bourges-Maunoury in Sèvres, a Paris suburb, at the same time. These were secret negotiations among the British, French, and Israeli leaders to initiate war against Nasser's Egypt. It all makes sense. Moscow has been sending arms to Nasser for more than a year now. Reportedly, Zhukov was in Cairo just last week."

Bissell stood, faster than he wanted. "What in hell is going on? I know the British and the French are apoplectic about Egypt's decision to toss the British out and nationalize the Suez Canal, but an invasion of Egypt? Is that what you think is happening? Are all three of them in on it?"

Dulles reached for his pipe like a child clutching a Teddy bear. "Yes, and yes. The Israelis are complaining about Egyptian fedayeen attacks. The French absolutely want Nasser deposed because of his support of the Algerian rebels. The Brits want the oil. Our U-2s are back in the good graces of Eisenhower. Detachment B at Adana and Detachment A from Wiesbaden and Giebelstadt have been doing constant overflights of the Middle East, as you know, and here's what they show as of October 28."

Dulles handed Bissell a report.

1. The French have relocated two squadrons of frontline jet fighters to Israel, which significantly exceeds the number the French are permitted to transfer under the Tripartite Declaration of 1950.

147

2. High-resolution photos show large quantities of weapons being loaded onto French and British ships in Toulon, Malta, and Cypress.

3. The British have located three aircraft carriers—the HMS *Eagle*, the *Bulwark*, and the *Albion*—in the Eastern Mediterranean, along with two renovated carriers acting as troop transports—the *Theseus* and the *Ocean*. South of the Suez, the British have positioned the cruiser HMS *Newfoundland*, which is accompanied by several French and British escort ships. These carriers have over a hundred Seahawk and Sea Venom fighter bombers, nine Wyvern attack planes, and eight AEW aircraft.

4. The French Navy has located two of its aircraft carriers in the Southeast Mediterranean, the Arromanches, and the Bois Belleau. These carriers are equipped with about forty F4U-Corsair fighter bombers and ten TBM Avenger anti-submarine aircraft.

5. U-2 photos have located eighteen tank and troop transport landing vessels. All together we've counted over 100 ships.

6. The Egyptian Navy has two former Hunt class destroyers, six frigates, and a small destroyer equivalent, all of which were acquired from Britain. They also have just recently acquired two more modern Soviet-built Skori-class destroyers, four armed minelayers, and twenty motor torpedo boats (MTBs).

7. The Israeli Navy consists of two former British Z-class destroyers, a frigate, several MTBs, and landing craft.

8. The US 6th Fleet—composed of fifty ships and 25,000 personnel, including 3,000 Marines along with 200 aircraft—is easily the most dominant force in the Southeast Mediterranean during this crisis. It is headed by two modernized Essex class aircraft carriers—the USS *Randolph* and the USS *Coral Sea*. In addition to the swept-wing F9F Cougar fighters, there is also a small

detachment of F2H Banshees capable of delivering nuclear weapons.

9. On October 29, Eisenhower sent two more aircraft carriers to the Mediterranean—the USS *Forrestal* and the USS *Franklin D. Roosevelt*. Admiral Derek, Chief of Naval Operations, sent a signal to Vice Admiral "Cat" Brown: "Situation tense; prepare for imminent hostilities." The vice admiral signaled back: "Am prepared for imminent hostilities. Whose side are we on?" Burke returned: "Keep clear of foreign areas, but take no guff from anybody."

10. The Egyptian Air Force is activated. It consists of 110 MiG-15 fighters and forty-eight IL-28 medium bombers, as well as older fighter aircraft.[84]

Bissell looked up, wide-eyed. "Well, I don't suppose all those ships are there getting ready for a regatta."

Dulles wanted to grin but resisted. "No, I don't think so."

Bissell paced around the room for a moment. "Where is Dr. Young? I haven't seen him for a few days now."

Dulles replied without looking up. "I sent him to Vienna on the 24th to cross the border into Hungary with some of our other agents."

"Okay. Where is he really?"

"Well, if he isn't dead, he should have reached the legation in Budapest by now."

"Holy Jesus, you're serious," Bissell said. "He's not a field agent. I doubt he knows which end of a revolver to hold."

"I imagine the world's preeminent theoretical physicist can figure out which end fires the bullet," Dulles said.

"Why in the world would you send him on such a dangerous mission?" Bissell asked. "You know that Eisenhower wants his opinion on the world situation even in peaceful times, but probably now more than ever."

Dulles knocked the ashes out of his pipe. "He came in here and begged to go. He knew the Agency had practically no one who can speak Hungarian. He knew it from when he worked with Leo Szilard, Edward Teller, John von Neumann, and John Kemeny on the Manhattan Project. So I let him go."

Bissell's laugh was nervous. "Well, I hope nothing happens to Ike's fair-haired boy, or you and I could be in for another five-star ass-chewing."

Dulles locked onto his assistant with a steely gaze. "More like a five-man firing squad," he said.

Bissell didn't smile.

19

October 27, 1956 – 0656 Hours
Freedom Fighters HQ
Esztergom, Hungary
(46 Kilometers NW of Budapest)

The rising sun on the Danube painted a much more pleasant picture than the grim faces in the room. Lieutenant Colonel Sander Bazso and Major Adorjan finalized their plans for their armored convoy's trip to Budapest. The major wanted to join the uprising that had ousted the unpopular communist leader Matyas Rakosi. Caleb Young had infiltrated the border between Austria and Hungary about twelve hours earlier and made his way to Esztergom based on intelligence from other CIA agents in Vienna.

Major Adorjan spoke to a small group. "This won't be easy, but the time is right, Colonel. We can't sit by and lose this opportunity created by the students and other citizens. We have the power to make this movement succeed. I know our rank and file supports us. We are all tired of the Russians running our country into the ground."

Colonel Bazso rallied from thought. "We are gambling everyone's life in our caserne. They are eager to fight, but our armor will only take us so far. Unless NATO forces support us—at least diplomatically—the Russians will regroup and crush us. I am not as sure as Imre Nagy that the US or NATO forces will risk a general war or even a tactical confrontation with the Russians to save us."

Despite their misgivings, the two officers ousted the Soviet troops and local Hungarian AVH secret police from Esztergom. Per Nagy's instructions, they led their troops, along with an array of forty T-34/85 tanks and Soviet armored vehicles, toward Budapest 46 kilometers to the southeast. Caleb made his way to the US legation from the outskirts of Budapest. Over the next two weeks, he witnessed the complete failure of the Western world's leaders to embrace a semblance of what they purported to stand for in any meaningful way.

The legation staff consisted of Charge d'Affaires Spencer Barnes, Tom Rogers, and military attaché Kerry Todd. They were awaiting the arrival of the new minister, Edward Wailes, when Caleb arrived. Against their advice, Caleb slipped out several nights to learn what he could from the local freedom fighters in Budapest. They had a realistic attitude concerning the military situation. They knew they could not hold off the Russians indefinitely if Khrushchev decided to crush them, but they were genuinely sanguine about the possibility of world opinion forcing the Soviets into withdrawing their troops, recognizing their neutrality.

On the evening of the 29th, Caleb contacted Nagy, who agreed to receive him once he told him about the American legation. For a man who was staring down the turret of a modern tank, Nagy seemed rather upbeat.

After Caleb found out what Nagy was planning, he got right to the point. "Premier Nagy, you cannot make a declaration of neutrality and secede from the Warsaw Pact. The Eisenhower Administration has given Moscow the green light to come in and crush you in exchange for staying out of Egypt. And if you deliver your speech tomorrow, no amount of suffering, bloodshed, or war crimes on the part of the Soviets will sway world opinion enough to stop them."[85]

Nagy disagreed politely, even after Caleb went over the US position as enunciated by Secretary of Defense Wilson and John Foster Dulles. So Caleb left.

When Colonel Bazso's forces arrived in Budapest, they were greeted as conquering heroes. At sunset on October 28, two divisions of Russian mechanized forces withdrew from Budapest, having suffered severe casualties during the previous five days due to a lack of infantry protection from the freedom fighters' Molotov cocktails and hand grenades. The events in Moscow and Washington over the next three days would determine the fate of not only the Eastern Bloc countries but also to a lesser degree the nascent student unrest within the Soviet Union.

The Hungarian people had listened to Radio Free Europe's broadcast of Eisenhower's campaign speeches about rolling back the Iron Curtain, a stark departure from Truman's policy of containment. In February 1956, Khrushchev had denounced Stalin and the Great Purge at the Communist Party's Twelfth Congress. The events emboldened Poland. In the late summer of 1956, the Poles had driven out the Stalinist hardliners and installed a path to socialism. It wasn't easy, and Polish leader Wladyslaw Gomulka had to defy Khrushchev, Bulganin, Molotov, and several other Politburo leaders at the Warsaw Airport as Soviet troops surrounded the city. Just as it looked like the Soviet Army was going to clash with the Polish Army, they reached a compromise.

The basics of that compromise eluded Imre Nagy. Gomulka had been able to control the radicals in Poland, calling for a complete break with Moscow, a turn of events the Russians would never have accepted. Poland agreed to remain a member of the Warsaw Pact and pursue its own brand of socialism. Nagy failed to learn from what Gomulka had done. He didn't rein in his hard-liners who sought neutrality and the removal of all Soviet troops. And Eisenhower hung him out to dry. The President was more interested in his stature as a statesman and his subsequent reelection than in taking a firm stance with the Soviets who were frightened by American nuclear power. Updated attack mapping had found 820 targets inside Russia, which would have resulted in more than 150 million deaths in the event of a US preemptive strike. But that was a bridge too far for the American public, and Ike knew it.

The US arsenal had an inventory of 3,692 nuclear weapons with a yield of over 10,000 megatons. The Soviet Union had 426 nuclear weapons with a yield of less than 10 percent of US weapons. The United States had 170 active B-52s, 188 B-36s, and 1,426 B-47s, all nuclear-capable. There were more than 350 Navy planes on aircraft carriers that were nuclear-ready and capable of hitting Russia and China. The Soviets had fewer than 100 Tu-95 Bears, their only round-trip bomber capable of reaching the United States, and no carriers or subs with the ability to deliver a nuclear bomb, given the U.S. Navy's blue water dominance.

Still, Eisenhower, who had not been shy about rattling the nuclear saber in other situations such as Korea, went out of his way to give the Soviets the all clear both through his own speeches and by way of instructions to John Foster Dulles and Henry Cabot Lodge, the UN Ambassador. The President wanted to ensure that the Soviets had a free hand in Hungary. He even had the US Ambassador in Moscow meet with Zhukov to tell him we would not interfere in Hungary.

But when Khrushchev threatened the Western Powers over Egypt, Ike told his advisors to inform them that if they even moved a muscle in Egypt, "we will hit them with both buckets." A more aggressive policy for Hungary would have significantly impacted what was decided in Moscow. In effect, nuclear diplomacy would have worked, given the huge disparity.

20

October 28, 1956 – 0845 Hours
Presidium Session
Communist Party Soviet Union (CPSU)
Central Committee (CC)
The Kremlin, Moscow, Russia

Nikita Khrushchev always looked angry, even when he smiled. It was something in his eyes—a malevolence even the broadest grin could not override.

"The matter in Hungary is becoming more complicated," Khrushchev said. "They're planning a demonstration. Prime Minister Janos Kadar is leaning toward negotiating with the centers of resistance."

Vyacheslav Molotov, Russia's Minister of Foreign Affairs and a man not particularly encouraged by the gasoline bottle bombs bearing his name in the streets of Budapest, sucked on the end of a pencil for a moment. "Things are going badly," he said. "The situation has deteriorated and is gradually moving toward capitulation. Nagy is speaking against us. We must have assurances of their friendship and an agreement for our troops to remain."

Lazar Kaganovich, Deputy First Secretary, picked at a spot on his arm. "Kadar should make concessions to the workers and peasants, nothing significant but enough to neutralize the movement. We need decisive action against hot spots. We cannot retreat."

Georgy Zhukov, the ever-pugnacious and territorial Defense Secretary, bristled. "Our troops are always ready, and we never retreat."

"Gentlemen, let's deal with the situation as it stands," Khrushchev said. "Will we have a government in Hungary that is with us, or will we have one determined for us to remove our troops? And if the Hungarians insist on our departure, what then? The uprising has spread into the provinces; it is possible that the Hungarian troops could support the insurgents." He paused to allow anyone foolish enough to speak to have time to reconsider. When no one moved, he continued. "There are two possibilities as I see it. The government acts, and we help— something we can complete quickly. Or Interior Secretary Nagy defies us, demands a cease-fire, and insists on troop withdrawal and capitulation. What are our alternatives?"[86]

Someone suggested that a committee take charge.

Khrushchev rolled his eyes.

A voice from the corner—"Retain this government, and send officials into the provinces. We could construct a reform platform and appeal to the population."

The suggestion barely registered.

"Could we ask others to appeal on our behalf—the Chinese, the Bulgarians, the Poles?"

There was a rumble of disapproval, and at least one person said something about "solving our own problems."

"Direct military intervention designed to suppress the insurgents is always an option," Khrushchev said. "But we will wait until Comrade Suslov returns from the scene. Then we will decide."

Seven hours later, Mikhail Suslov made his report. "There are 350 dead Hungarians and 3,000 wounded. We have 600 dead. The public opinion of our troops has gotten worse. Seventy ordinary citizens were killed at the radio station demonstration on October 24th. Workers left their assignments in protest. Spontaneous councils have sprouted in various cities. The demonstrations are markedly anti-Soviet sentiment. Yesterday, they formed a government. Nagy insisted on troop withdrawal."

Military legend Kliment Voroshilov bristled. "We acted correctly when we sent in troops. We should be in no hurry to pull them out. American secret services are everywhere. A group of comrades should go there, form a government, and cement our hand. Only then do we consider moving any troops. We sent you there for nothing!"

Khrushchev's voice was a low growl. "Your criticism is unwarranted and too severe. Comrade Suslov has done well, and we are grateful for his evaluation of a difficult situation."

Voroshilov was sharp enough to understand when he was being told to shut down. He sulked in his seat but said nothing.

After Khrushchev's admonishment, every man fell in line. Support the new government, avoid looking like an occupational force, appeal to the fraternal parties and the citizens, and on and on.

But everything hinged on a cease-fire in the hot zones.

On October 28, the Presidium was in full support of the Nagy government's request for a cease-fire, the dissolution of the secret police, and the commencement of negotiations on Soviet troop withdrawals.

Two days later, the Presidium approved a Declaration by the Government of the USSR on the Principles of Development and Further Strengthening of Friendship and Cooperation between the Soviet Union and Other Socialist States. It opened the possibility of a Soviet troop withdrawal from Hungary as well as other East European satellites.

Khrushchev announced the vote and smiled as he spoke. "We must choose between a military path of occupation and a peaceful one with the withdrawal of troops and negotiations."

The hard-liners had been moved aside.

It was a turning point . . . or so it seemed.

Some in Nagy's inner circle smelled blood in the water and overplayed their hand. They pressed for Hungary's neutrality and a withdrawal from the Warsaw Pact.[87]

A week later, following another vote by a now-incensed Presidium, more than 5,000 Soviet tanks supported by twelve military divisions rumbled into Hungary and crushed a gaggle of freedom fighters who up to the very last day (or their last breath) hoped for NATO to rescue them.

That never happened.

21

November 21, 1956
Office of Deputy Director of
Intelligence, Robert Amory Jr.
CIA Headquarters
Langley, Virginia

When Caleb returned to Langley from the legation in Hungary on November 21, he learned the Russians had not withdrawn. Instead, they had rained armored havoc on their Warsaw Pact colleague. At the Agency, Robert Amory suggested to the NSC planning staff that "as soon as it becomes clear that the Russians, instead of withdrawing, are pouring reinforcements into Hungary, we should give the Soviet Union an ultimatum either to keep their hands off Hungary or we will not be responsible for whatever happens next."

Amory wanted to interdict rail and road connections into Hungary with a surgical nuclear strike limited to Lvov in Poland and selected passes in the mountains of Russian Ruthenia and Western Romania. Dulles told him to talk with Bowie in military planning about it, but the idea was DOA. After all, everyone knew about the speech Dulles gave in Dallas on October 27.

> Let me make this clear, beyond the possibility of a doubt: the United States has no ulterior purposes in desiring the independence of the satellite countries. . . . We do not look upon these nations as potential military allies.[88]

On October 28, when Secretary of Defense Wilson was asked on *Face the Nation* about the turmoil in Hungary, he said, "Developments in Poland and Hungary would not cause any revision in the US defense posture." He categorically ruled out any American military involvement.

The hands-off opinion was echoed by Eisenhower on November 1. He said it would be hypocritical to criticize the Russians in Hungary and support the British and the French in Egypt. He was easily reelected. Perhaps the final straw came when Henry Cabot Lodge, the US Ambassador to the UN, opposed the Hungarian questions transfer to the General Assembly, most likely because he wanted the Egyptian problem on the front burner.

As far as Caleb was concerned, this was one of the sadder chapters in American history. Sure, America gained a great measure of prestige around the world by taking the high road in Egypt when they forced the British to stop their advance on November 7 by threatening economic ruin of England's currency, the pound sterling. Due to U-2 flights, Eisenhower knew almost the exact moment when British carrier planes destroyed most of the Egyptian Air Force while it was on the ground. But after touring the city and countryside in Hungary and seeing the damage done to a nation of ten million that only desired what Americans take for granted, Caleb was depressed by how Eisenhower handled the situation. *Maybe he was spot on,* Caleb thought. *Who the hell knows?*

A hands-off situation would have worked if only Nagy hadn't overplayed his hand and pushed the Russians to reduce Budapest to a mass of rubble. There would not have been 2,600 dead Hungarians, and Caleb knew that two of them might have been his parents. He had been searching for them unsuccessfully since they disappeared in Hungary in 1951.

But once the Russian bear roared without opposition, Khrushchev wasted no time stepping into the spotlight.

22

November 18, 1956 – 1423 Hours
Polish Embassy
Moscow, Russia

The Western Bloc nations listened as Khrushchev's voice filled the hall at the Polish Embassy. "About the capitalist states, it doesn't depend on you whether or not we exist. If you don't like us, don't accept our invitations, and don't invite us to come to you. Whether you like it or not, history is on our side. *We will bury you.*"[89]

Close to a dozen Western diplomats left the room. A few who didn't take the First Secretary seriously started to laugh. Khrushchev got in trouble with some members of the Presidium who did not take kindly to his remark and chided him for being so offensive. Khrushchev claimed he was only referring to a Marxist saying that "the proletariat is the undertaker of capitalism."

No one outside of the Kremlin bought what he was trying to sell.

∽

November and December, 1956

Even though the entire U-2 Agency team had performed well above Eisenhower's expectations in the Middle East, the President did not authorize another mission until November 20. The outing was a peripheral penetration, something the Agency and the Joint Chiefs of Staff had long been advocating.

On December 10, 1956, two more flights were authorized over Bulgaria. During all three, Soviet fighters attempted in vain to reach attack altitude. None got within 15,000 feet. Meanwhile, the Air Force modified an RB-57D to perform what they told Eisenhower would be "an undetected high-speed trip" over the far eastern coast of the Soviet Union to photograph the city of Vladivostok.[90]

The plane was detected. The Soviets issued a loud, formal protest to the American Embassy in Moscow. US Ambassador Bohlen sent Ike a cable and warned of another potential Berlin blockade if the flights continued.

The threat was all it took.

On December 18, 1956, Eisenhower ordered "a complete stoppage of this entire business." Not even peripheral border flights were allowed again until March 18, 1957, when the new system V Electronics gathering apparatus replaced the camera.

The new system was very heavy. It collected data from nine wave bands. System 1 had been limited to the S and X frequency bands. Because of its obvious disadvantage in gross weight, System V was used for only three missions.

But another issue loomed. The secrecy surrounding the U-2 was about to come to an end.

⸎

On April 2, 1957, Robert Sieker, participating in Operation Rainbow, crashed an Article 341 prototype in such a remote area of Area 51 in the Nevada desert that it took four days to find the plane. The search for the plane attracted the attention of the press. A story published in the North American newspaper *Alliance* stated that the United States had a craft capable of operating at altitudes above 65,000 feet. It was being utilized by the United States to find targets for its guided missile program. Not long after, *The London Daily News* let fly with another volley. "Lockheed's U-2 Hi-Altitude aircrafts of the U.S. Air Force have been flying at 65,000 feet, out of the reach of Soviet interceptors, mapping large areas behind the Iron Curtain with revolutionary new aerial cameras. They are making mathematically precise maps essential to bombardment with missile weapons."[91]

The cat was out of the bag. But as Dulles wryly noted, "It had been kicking and making a fuss for the last nine months, so somebody was bound to see it sooner or later." Despite all the publicity, Washington remained mum. After Khrushchev saw the newspapers, he called in his Commander-in-Chief of the Air Defense Forces, Sergey Biryuzov.

"Comrade Biryuzov, can you not see that the whole world is laughing at us?" Khrushchev bellowed. "Are we so incompetent that we cannot even shoot a simple airplane out of the sky? Do we have to wait for the American bombers and missiles to destroy our entire country?"

Biryuzov, fully aware of the possibility of impending personal doom, got defensive. "First Secretary Khrushchev, we have completed numerous new radar installations equipped with our latest C-75 Dvina surface-to-air missiles. It is merely a matter of time before the Americans run out of luck and feel the heat of our new missiles, which can reach 25,000 meters."

"But Comrade Biryuzov, they are able to detect your tracking of them, and then they simply change course once they detect your radar."

"Comrade Khrushchev, we are rapidly deploying new mobile radar installations around our production facilities and missile testing areas. We know where they are going to go even before they do."

"Comrade Biryuzov, I need to shoot down the American spy planes soon. They will not stop until you shoot them down and we can prove that the Americans are behind this. If they discover our true state of readiness, they will attack us like imperialists always do to enslave weaker countries. We will have to shoot off some of the few missiles we have to make them think we are ready for them."

The Soviets unsuccessfully tested ICBMs on May 15 and June 11, 1957. June 11 was the same date of the United States' first unsuccessful test. It was clear that the missile age had arrived when on August 21, 1957, the Soviets fired an R-7 Semyorka a distance of 3,700 miles. It was just a matter of time before weapons would be mounted on the missiles, imperiling human civilization for decades to come. Ironically, those who had created the danger sought to put the genie back in the bottle.

23

July 8, 1957 – 0800 Hours
Thinkers Lodge – 247 Water Street
Pugwash, Nova Scotia

Bertrand Russell's letter to the Conference was read to open the meeting:

Almost exactly two years have passed since the statement was issued, signed by the late Albert Einstein, some eight other colleagues and myself, drawing attention to the dangers that would face humanity if another world war were to break out, with the almost certainty of the widespread use of nuclear weapons. In that statement we drew attention to the need for competent scientists to assemble in conference, so that a true assessment of these dangers could be made. The two years that have elapsed since that statement was issued have not seen any fundamental change in the situation. In fact the stock piles of nuclear weapons have increased, new nations have joined the ranks of those producing these weapons – or trying to produce them – while serious misgivings have been expressed as to whether even the continued testing of such weapons may not result in damage to the population.[92]

Joseph Rotblat, who was Secretary-General of the Pugwash Conferences on Science and World Affairs, suggested that all twenty-two attendees should check their political opinions at the door and seriously consider the dangers of a nuclear war. In addition to the physicists who attended, a few social scientists and financial sponsors had made their way to the large island in Eastern Canada. Professor Iwao Ogawa and Dr. Caleb Young from the United States gave a two-hour primer to the social scientists on day one in the morning to prepare them for the more technical aspects of the conference.

Professor Ogawa, a Nobel Prize winner in Physics from the Rikkyo University in Japan, conducted a session on the basics of nuclear theory and the damage Hiroshima and Nagasaki suffered from the small fission bombs dropped at the end of World War II. He began. "I am not here to criticize the United States' decision to use nuclear weapons against Japan. I want to give some of our invitees who are not physicists a rudimentary understanding of fission, fusion, nuclear weaponry, and their effect upon human existence from ground zero to distances as far away as 200 miles. Let's first draw on what we know about the results of the use of nuclear weapons. You can also find a general summary of what we will talk about in Appendix I."

Ogawa was both professorial and interesting. He knew his audience and understood he could get technical without losing them. Indeed, most of his listeners were thirsting to know as much as they could about the new and terrible power possessing simultaneous promises of hope and desolation. He ran through a brief discussion of isotopes and atomic weight and then moved on to the meat of his presentation.

"Fission involves propelling a neutron at a high speed into the nucleus of a uranium-235 amu isotope. The 'attack' splits the nucleus into two lighter nuclei. Chemically speaking, given the original target of U-235, we will most likely end up with Barium 141/56 plus Krypton 92/36 and three free neutrons. A sufficient supply of the uranium fuel will result in a chain reaction where more than one neutron is released by each dividing nucleus."

The social scientists in the audience hung onto every word. To most of them, the presentation sounded like something Ming the Merciless would have concocted in the *Flash Gordon* serials of their youth.

"Fusion occurs when two light nuclei combine to produce a heavier, more stable nucleus. Deuterium fusion is when you force two hydrogen atoms together to produce a helium nucleus with one neutron and two protons. That produces a free neutron that continues a chain reaction. Remember, those hydrogen protons are both positive charges. They don't like each other, so we need to have a shotgun wedding."

The audience laughed quietly.

Ogawa smiled. "The shotgun is a fission reaction with enough force to push them to the altar where they both say 'I do.' The baby from this union doesn't take nine months to appear or even nine milliseconds for that matter. It shows up instantaneously and is named 'neutron.' It has a lot of energy—a bouncing baby neutron!"

There was more laughter, a little louder.

"A chain reaction ensues, one with a lot more bang for your buck. A fusion bomb can produce 1,000 times the energy of a fissionable device while using an equivalent quantity of matter. A hydrogen bomb, a fusion device, weighs much less than a comparable fission bomb. I have no doubt we will soon have the damnable capacity to deliver them over great distances, perhaps even from submarines."

The tittering stopped. A deadly quiet seized every listener.

"Let's talk about the comparatively miniscule destructive power of the fission bomb. On July 16, 1945, the test bomb produced an explosion equivalent to 21 kilotons of TNT, or 88 TJ. The explosion created a mushroom cloud 12 kilometers high and left a 1.5-meter-deep crater with a diameter of 80 meters. The shockwave was felt more than 160 kilometers from ground zero. The 15 kiloton fission bomb dropped on Hiroshima had the following effects." Ogawa read from a list.

1. Static overpressure of 5 psi over a 9.44 kilometer area, fatal to the unprotected. The hydrodynamic front at ground zero produced winds in excess of 700 miles per hour.

2. Thermal radiation causing third-degree burns over a 10.7 kilometer area, often fatal.

3. A fatal ionizing radiation radius lasting 24 hours and covering a 4 kilometer area.

4. About 80,000 deaths within the first minute and another 55,000 to date from fires and sickness within a city having a population of 255,260.

5. Residual radiation of up to 100 rems covering an area of more than 15 kilometers from the epicenter, causing sickness but not death.

Everyone knew they were hearing what could be considered an announcement of the end of the world.

Ogawa continued. "The decentralization of the command decision of when and how to use tactical nuclear weapons is the most likely catalyst for the genesis of a general war among nuclear powers. A local field commander could misinterpret a military action by a foe, either by accident or from malice. Perhaps a green officer panics and believes he is about to be overrun when, in reality, what he sees is a routine field exercise. The consequences will be terrible."

The lecturer's face reflected the gravity of his words. He looked drawn, almost terrified.

"There is another, perhaps more insidious, scenario," Ogawa said. "Hardliners in government could make the decision to strike hard and strike first, to land the proverbial knock-out blow." He paused. "Hear this . . . and etch it on your hearts. There can be no 'successful' first strike. Retaliation will be swift, certain, and unavoidable. Once *any nation* launches a nuclear weapon, Armageddon will surely follow.

"While no one can predict the side effects of a full-scale nuclear war with any certainty, my estimates involve 10,000 megatons of nuclear devices and include TNWs—submarine-based, medium-range, ICBMs, and everything in between.

"There are a great many concerns other than the immediate number of casualties, such as potentially irreparable damage to the atmosphere from dirt, soot, and radiation. Localized and residual fallout will certainly eventuate in genetic cancers and long-term health issues—perhaps the total collapse of every known healthcare system in the world.

"The fission nuclear bombs dropped on Japan totaled less than 37 kilotons and produced 300,000 deaths. An exchange involving 10,000 megatons aimed in considerable part at the population centers would produce a death toll of at least 150 million in the first twenty-four hours. Over the following thirty days, you could expect at least another fifty million deaths. It's hard to imagine, but many military leaders in the NATO and Warsaw Pacts have publicly stated that they believe there will be a conventional war after the nuclear exchanges. Friends and colleagues, if someone launches one of these damnable devices, the only armies left will be roving bands of stick-wielding warriors trying to find water that is suitable to drink."

Ogawa spent time on the optimal height for detonations, a refreshing shift to technical information, and then went back to hammering the audience with the awful realities of a nuclear conflict.

"At a 5 kilometer HOB," Ogawa continued, "a 20 megaton weapon detonated over the center of New York City would produce static overpressure of 20 psi over a 7.62 kilometer radius or an area of 183 kilometers, destroying everything, including concrete-reinforced buildings. The mushroom cloud would be 34.3 kilometers high with a diameter of 102 kilometers. The height of the fireball would be 10.8 kilometers with a radius of 3.2 kilometers. The heat would cause the surrounding air *to burn.* One hundred percent of the people within a 38.4 kilometer radius (an area of 4,640 kilometers) would suffer third-degree burns. For those of you who have forgotten your first aid training, a third-degree burn destroys both the dermis and the epidermis. It likely will damage the underlying bones, muscles, and tendons. There is no sensation because the nerve endings are destroyed.

"For those fortunate enough to survive the static overpressure by being in a fortified bomb shelter or far enough from the blast and thermal radiation, there will still be residual radiation effects. For our purposes, all distances are from ground zero or in a straight line from the epicenter (for an airburst) to the ground before we start measuring. The distances are approximations, and some of what I will say comes under the heading of an educated guess. Whether you die from radiation or get sick and recover depends on too many variables to cover in our short presentation, but here are some ideas.

"As you can imagine, after a nuclear blast, there are all kinds of unstable atoms possessing an excess of energy or mass or both. To reach stability, these atoms give off, or emit, the excess energy or mass. This excess energy can be emitted from the nucleus as gamma radiation, transferred to one of its electrons to release it as a conversion electron, or used to create an alpha particle or beta particle. These emissions are called radiation. Radioactivity refers to the amount of ionizing-harmful radiation, which represents how many atoms there are in the material decay in a given time period.[93]

"We measure the amount of radiation in a cubic centimeter of dry air in Roentgens. If you have 1 Roentgen in a cubic centimeter of air, that is enough to set free one electrostatic unit of charge. Still, we are most concerned with how any radioactivity affects the body, particularly in a cumulative amount. An extremely high dose absorbed in a few hours can be just as deadly as a lower dose over a week or several months. We measure absorption in the body by rads or rems.

"Rad stands for radiation absorbed dose. One rad equals a dose causing 100 ergs of energy to be absorbed by one gram of matter, the same as the amount of energy used by a common house fly performing one pushup. The rad is the measurement of the radiation absorbed by the material or tissue, while the rem is a measurement of the biological effect of the absorbed radiation. For beta and gamma radiation, the dose equivalent is the same as the absorbed dose, so one rad is equal to one rem. By contrast, the equivalent is larger than the absorbed dose for alpha and neutron radiation because these types of radiation are more damaging to the human body per unit absorbed. So we are primarily concerned with rems because they give us the best indication of biological harm."[94]

Ogawa nodded, and several slides flicked across the screen behind him in rapid succession. For those in the audience who still didn't understand the grim realities of radiation exposure, the images may have seemed like creations of Hollywood makeup artists. The audience was, without exception, men of science. But still, Ogawa noticed more than a few squirming in their seats, perhaps wondering if the images on the slides were real. One pasty-faced fellow near the back bolted for the door, undoubtedly for the restroom.

"I'll not belabor my talk with too many more statistics, but it is imperative to understand the following," Ogawa said. "Theoretically, if a person is not killed by the blast or thermal radiation or chooses to render aid within certain areas, those exposed to 1,000 rem will die within four to six days. Anyone who encounters 600 rem will likely die, and out of those who do survive, 18 percent of them will die of cancer. Anyone getting 500 rem exposure will likely die within thirty days. The residual radiation that will be carried up into the mushroom cloud and then spread over several hundred kilometers downwind will ultimately kill hundreds of thousands if not millions over the next year. My estimate of the immediate deaths within the greater New York City area is four million. Longer term, that number will likely exceed five million.

"In short, a thermonuclear explosion is a death sentence to many, and those who do not die will probably wish they had."

Dr. Young stood up. "I have nothing to add to the science part of this, but I am going to say a few words about the weapons. It isn't any secret that the Soviets and the United States are testing ICBMs. Both will be successful within two years. The next step is to mount one of these relatively much smaller and more powerful fusion bombs to a reentry vehicle. Then we will have exponentially more problems keeping our leaders and our military from surprise preemptive attacks. Picture the TNW situation that Dr. Ogawa described in a standoff over Berlin, and we are all finished."

24

June 1964
Office of William Forde, Esq., Chief of
the Criminal Division and CIA Liaison
950 Pennsylvania Avenue, Suite 710
Washington, DC

Forde stifled an involuntary shudder. "You're telling me that the outbreak of a nuclear war would result in twenty-five million deaths within sixty days?"

"No," Caleb said. "I'm saying there would be that many in the United States. Europe and Asia would suffer ten times as many. Have you read Kissinger's 1958 book on nuclear weapons and foreign diplomacy?"

"Should I have?"

"No," Caleb responded quickly, "but for our discussion, you need to understand Kissinger's theories. Kissinger is Nelson Rockefeller's protégé on the Council of Foreign Relations. The faculty at Harvard couldn't stand him any longer and wouldn't renew his contract."

"He's as arrogant as you are, Doctor?"

Caleb ignored the jab and continued. "Kissinger's theory boils down to 'strategic ambiguity,' essentially a game of blind man's bluff. What that means is that if you're going to play the game of escalation dominance, you have to convince the opposite side that you will play the last card—preemptive nuclear war."

"Holy Mother of God!"

"Nothing holy about it, Mr. Forde."

Forde took a minute to right the ship. "Okay, enough science. Let's get to the reason you are here."

"It's only taken about four months," Caleb said. "All this time I thought you wanted to talk with me because of my engaging conversational style."

Forde didn't bite at the sarcasm. He was still shaken by the thought of 10 percent of the world's population disappearing in the span of two short months. Getting back on topic, Forde stated, "Both Katzenbach and Hoover think you passed submarine missile technology information through Colonel Penkovsky to the GRU, the Russian Chief Intelligence Office."

"I met the Colonel at Lac-Beauport, Quebec, during the 1958 conference. He was not yet the 'official liaison, caretaker for the scientists.' He was just along for the ride. Our initial contact was over dinner on April 7, 1958. Subsequently, I met with him many times. I was always accompanied by an Agency agent, so there is nothing to hide. We gathered intel on their submarine ballistic missile program and other information on how to detect and follow their submarines. It proved most useful during the Cuban Missile Crisis. As you know, MI6 has thousands of pages of transcripts from their interviews. Back then, despite the Soviets having less than 20 percent of the missiles and bombers we had, we were a paranoid nation driven by the press. And even now you persist in this witch hunt."

"You know MI6 believes you acted as a double agent and compromised NATO defenses?" Forde asked. "And there was the October 28th incident."

"When a Russian sub armed with a nuclear-tipped torpedo came within range of several of our ships? That one?"

"Yes. Almost started World War III," Forde said.

"Mr. Forde, you have no idea how hard it is to go through life surrounded by idiots—present company excepted."

Forde sucked on the inside of his upper lip. "Well, deeply appreciated compliment aside, would you care to comment on the October 28th debacle?"

"Certainly," Caleb said. "It was the Navy's fault. The swabbies used the wrong version of our sonar. They did not monitor the frequency the Agency had given them for Soviet communications. I passed along information about the nuclear torpedo, but no one at ONI wanted to believe it, and they still don't." Caleb paused. "Besides, the Colonel was executed in 1962 for *helping us.* He gave us much more information on the *science* of nuclear weapons in history than I ever shared with him. Don't forget—MI6 has more than 3,000 pages of transcripts from his interviews. I've read all of them. I am mentioned exactly never!"

Forde tried to look inscrutable. He couldn't pull it off. "Hoover says otherwise," he said.

"You cannot bluff your way into information," Caleb said. "I didn't do anything wrong, and we both know it. If you knew anything, we would not have danced around this table for this long."

∽

<h1 style="text-align:center">March 15, 1958
GRU Headquarters ("The Aquarium")
Khodynka Airfield
Moscow, Russia</h1>

"Good morning, Colonel Penkovsky. I have a new assignment for you. You are to accompany our scientific delegation to the Second Annual Pugwash Peace Conference in Lac-Beauport, Quebec, Canada. You will be directly responsible for seeing that they do not communicate with Western scientists other than through their official presentations, the contents of which you have already reviewed. Be discreet. The Western press loves to characterize us as a closed society with no respect for individual freedoms. We have several of our best scientists going, including Dr. Skobeltsyn and Dr. Topchiev. You are the best scientist in the GRU. You understand the importance of these meetings."

"Is that all, General?"

"No. One more thing. We want you to observe the American delegation very carefully. We have reason to believe one of their scientists has been an agent of the CIA since the Second World War. He even may have worked on the Manhattan Project—a Dr. Caleb Young. There is a picture in the dossier. You won't have any trouble finding him. He is quite tall—a basketball player as I understand. We cannot ascertain his affiliation with any academic institution. We believe he has been with the CIA for some time."

"Thank you, General. One question. What is our official response to Western claims that we are serially producing missiles and hydrogen weapons like 'sausages,' per Chairman Khrushchev's statements? As you know, I've sat in on defense meetings at the Central Committee, and for the most part, my advice to improve our radar and coordinate it with our SAMs has been followed. We also have invested most of our resources in other defensive weapons such as tens of thousands of fighter planes to repel the Western heavy bombers. Still, Chairman Khrushchev continues to poke the United States in the eye every chance he gets by boasting about our missile and hydrogen bomb superiority, something that does not exist to my knowledge."

"Colonel, your job is to deliver the correct message at the Pugwash Conference despite the Premier's comments to the contrary. What we want is world peace. The Americans are developing massive numbers of offensive weapons. We cannot control Khrushchev. He will continue bluffing until we convince their military leaders of our invincibility. Then—and only then—will they leave us alone."

"General, we cannot even stop their spy planes, let alone bombers and missiles."

"Colonel, we will make them pay for their transgressions soon enough. That is all."

Colonel Penkovsky left the office, shaking his head over the dangerous game of blind man's bluff. He believed Khrushchev was sending the wrong message to a nation that had ramped up military production to unequaled levels during World War II and could undoubtedly do it again.

This is insanity, he thought. *Utter, inexcusable insanity.*

25

August 21, 1957 – 0627 Hours
Tyuratam Railhead Station
Kazakhstan

No one liked talking to Sergei Shtemenko. This head of the GRU could frighten someone just by saying Happy Birthday. After all, sometimes he followed the greeting with the words, "This is the last one you will ever have."

"Comrade Korolev," Shtemenko asked, "are you certain this missile, as modified, will fly over 5,000 kilometers?"

"I am," Sergei Korolev said. The chief Soviet missile designer felt his sphincter tighten. He'd already been arrested in 1938. Though hell was not a concept "good communists" were supposed to hold, his time in Lubyanka Prison had solidified his belief in some form of eternal agony.

Shtemenko continued. "There was the Block D fire on May 15. It caused the rupture of a key rocket component, did it not?"

"A strap," Korolev said. "I am well aware of the results. It broke at T+88 seconds—"

Not to be outdone, Shtemenko finished the history. "And your 'wonder rocket' crashed 248 miles down-range. Then there was the electrical short on June 11—uncontrollable rolling and ultimate disintegration. Premier Khrushchev has a long memory about such failures."

As do you, you loathsome snake, Korolev thought. But he kept his face blank. Conversations with the GRU Director did nothing to soothe the rocket designer's nerves.

"Comrade Shtemenko," Korolev said, "I can assure you that all corrections have been made. The world will see the first intercontinental ballistic missile fly today."

Korolev stared at the massive missile outside the blockhouse. Powered by four strap-on liquid rocket boosters surrounding a central sustainer engine, the 112-foot monster dominated the landscape. Had he been allowed to believe in God, Korolev would have crossed himself. He held his breath instead.

The missile traveled more than 5,500 kilometers before splashing down in the Pacific Ocean.

⚬⚬⚬

Office of Defense Mobilization
Science Advisory Committee
Security Resources Panel – Gaither Committee

By January 1957, members of Congress were up in arms about the need for innumerable passive defense programs. Senators from Mississippi recalled the cries of "rats to your holes" that had echoed throughout the city of Vicksburg during the Union's bombardment in 1863. The natural comparisons between the godless communists and the damn Yankees were simply an unspoken, smile-inducing bonus.

It was the recommendation of the Federal Civil Defense Administration (FCDA) to spend $32 billion on a civil defense shelter program. The question, "Where are we going to get the money?" in an era where balanced budgets were considered the norm was never answered.

The National Defense budget totaled about $40 billion. Eisenhower, a fiscal conservative, balked at spending so extravagantly on a single program, especially one that was destined to make NATO allies wonder about the United States' commitment to the defense of Europe. In May 1957, after consulting with James Killian, his Chief Science Officer, and Robert Cutler, the Assistant for National Security Affairs, Eisenhower appointed H. Rowan Gaither to establish a committee of experts to study the rising nuclear threat and recommend a solution.

By early June, Gaither had assembled a formidable group of experts from the scientific community. Among them were weapons system analysts from the RAND Corporation and several distinguished scientists from the Lincoln Project's Technological Capabilities Panel (TCP). After the Soviets' successful ICBM launch, the committee, through a series of miscommunications among various subcommittee members and Cutler, began an examination of the effect of a massive surprise attack on America's ability to inflict enough damage in a retaliatory strike on the Soviet Union to make the Bear blink a few times. The committee members believed that once the Russians attained a preemptive capability, they would use it.

Charles Bohlen, the US Ambassador to Moscow for a major part of the Eisenhower Administration, said, "There is no important disagreement among policymakers that if matters reach the point where the Soviets attain the capability of delivering a decisive initial blow on the United States without serious risk to their own regime, they would do so."[95]

Bohlen and George Kennan were considered the foremost experts on the Soviet Union during the 1950s. By 1943, Bohlen had become head of the East European Division for the State Department and was one of six specialists assigned to begin a Russian language program. He served as the interpreter and advisor for both Roosevelt and Truman at the Potsdam and Yalta Conferences. In short, he knew the Soviet Union and its leaders.

In addition to agreeing with the "Soviets will do it if they can" theory, the TCP panel concluded that the US military leaders, with the exception of Eisenhower, were largely oblivious to the threat. They also found that maintaining an invulnerable counterstriking force would afford the option of a first strike without retaliation for the United States. James Killian's TCP Committee concluded:

> Our striking forces must blunt the attack at its source. The importance to the defense of the United States of an offensive air striking force stems from its ability to attack the Soviet

long-range Air Force on the ground. By being able to strike at the "source" or "on the ground," the United States would be capable of a preventive war or, at a minimum, a preemptive war.[96]

When Gaither fell ill in the middle of the study, Robert Sprague and William Foster took over the helm. Sprague had been a consultant to the National Security Council on Continental Defenses. He was increasingly alarmed by the possibility of a Soviet surprise attack. He believed the Soviet rulers lacked the moral character to care about the widespread death and destruction of an atomic war. Such realities were no detriment. He felt the Soviets were willing to suffer debilitating losses if the payoff was the destruction of the United States. He saw three solutions to the Soviet problem.

First, the United States could construct a defensive system capable of withstanding any possible Soviet attack. Second, it could strike the first blow. Third, it could live with the USSR in a state of equilibrium brought about by mutual fear of atomic attack.[97]

Another key advisor to the Gaither Committee, Colonel George Lincoln, was convinced that the first mover, because of the latest technological advances, had an unmistakable, almost insurmountable advantage.

The time element . . . has been magnified by modern technology in at least three ways. First, the race for technological advantage is decided before hostilities. Second, the aggressor has an increasing advantage paralleling the upward slant of technological change. Third, and related to the preceding point, the surprise aggression becomes more attractive and harder to meet.[98]

Paul Nitze painted an even bleaker picture.

In the event of a crisis involving a serious possibility of war with the United States, how might the problem be seen from the Kremlin? Being careful planners, the Soviets undoubtedly would have carefully prepared war plans for a variety of contingencies. One could therefore theorize with some confidence that Soviet plans would include a disarming first strike. If we responded with the remains of the Strategic Air Command by attacking Soviet base structure and nuclear attack facilities, the exchange ratios would go against us very quickly. In two, three, four, or at most five exchanges, the United States would be down to a woefully low level of capability while the Soviet Union could still be at a relatively high one. We would then be at their mercy. If we choose to attack their populations, we will invite almost total annihilation in the United States.[99]

In about the same time period, General Thomas D. White completed a presentation at the 1957 Air Force Commanders Annual Conference. He said a successful strategy in a future war was "to select and destroy a target system, the destruction of which is possible in the event of initiation of war by the United States or after a Soviet surprise attack."[100] White's presentation only confirmed the strategy Curtis LeMay had outlined at the National War College in 1954. "We think the best chance of preventing attacks on this country is to get those airplanes on the ground before they take off rather than depending on the Air Defense Command to shoot them down after they get here."[101]

◦◦◦

October 28, 1957 – 0900 Hours
SAC – Offut Air Force Base
Omaha, Nebraska

Robert Sprague had received a "tourist visit" about a month earlier, courtesy of the sullen LeMay who often didn't hide his disdain for the academics of the world. Sprague went to Eisenhower, distressed at the lack of readiness on the part of the SAC, considering it would take six hours to get an effective strike force off the ground. Ike was perturbed.

"General LeMay, this is an order," Eisenhower said. "You are to show Mr. Sprague to our war room at Offut."

Sprague returned on the 28th. "Come with me, Mr. Sprague," LeMay said.

LeMay took Sprague into a room that was fairly near the display that showed the response times for the SAC bombers was inadequate during a tactical attack. In a separate room behind the first, LeMay showed him where he was receiving his own intelligence. LeMay pointed out some of the many machines that were reading off messages that were coming in from SAC planes flying at various places around the world. LeMay went to a map of Russia and identified numerous planes that were flying around the perimeter of the Soviet Union and actually flying over Russia.

"I will know from my own intelligence," LeMay said, "whether the Russians are gathering their planes presumably for a massive attack against the United States. And if I come to that conclusion, I'm going to knock the shit out of them before they get off the ground."

"Oh, that isn't national policy," Sprague said. "You know that, don't you?"

"No. It's not a national policy. It's my policy."[102]

This made Sprague all the more uncomfortable. *Was LeMay going to consult Ike, the JCS, or anyone else before he "knocked the shit out of them"? What if he was wrong and it was merely a Soviet bluff or worse simply a new type of Soviet military exercise? The fact that LeMay knew the United States was vulnerable to a tactical attack might make him trigger-happy. Couldn't we do better than six hours to get our strike force airborne?*

Sprague considered this information so dangerous that he had only confided it to his chief deputy William Foster until the night before the presentation of the Gaither Report to the NSC. On November 6, Jim Douglas, the Secretary of the Air

Force, was courteous enough to have a meeting for the Steering Committee in his private dining room at the Pentagon. Sprague was seated to the right of Secretary Douglas, and LeMay was seated to Douglas's left.

"Mr. Secretary," Sprague said, "I presume you know that if we have a surprise attack against the SAC with only tactical warning, we would not be able to make a retaliatory response."

Douglas replied, "General LeMay, you have heard what Mr. Sprague said, and it's my knowledge and I guess general knowledge in the event of a surprise attack that we would have at least 168 bombers that would not be destroyed."

Before General LeMay could respond, Sprague interrupted and said, "Perhaps I did not phrase my question or inquiry correctly. What I am asking is not how many would be saved but how many would be in the position to make a retaliatory attack with full crews aboard, sufficient fuel, and weapons. I know the SAC has auxiliary civilian bases they can go to in the event of an attack, but they go with a limited crew and not enough fuel onboard to reach the enemy, and they wouldn't have access to any weapons because those weapons would have been destroyed at the SAC bases."[103]

Without waiting for Douglas to say anything, LeMay, with half a mouthful of food, said, "Mr. Sprague is correct."

Foster and Sprague decided to leave LeMay's policy and details of the woefully inadequate response time out of the final report and contacted Robert Cutler about what they considered a major problem. They requested a meeting with the President immediately after their main presentation on November 7. The presentation that day ended with a thud when the only comment that was elicited from the Administration was by DCI Allen Dulles who said, "Well, it's my experience that in a study of this kind, the group always overestimates the capabilities of Russia and underestimates our capability."[104]

The meeting with the President took place in the Oval Office immediately after the National Security Council meeting.

∞

November 7, 1957 – 1630 Hours
Oval Office, the White House
Washington, DC

Robert Sprague and William Foster entered the Oval Office for what they anticipated would be a private meeting with the President. When they arrived, they saw the Chiefs of Staff and the Chairman of the Joint Chiefs, along with Don Quarles, Undersecretary of Defense for Research and Development. Sprague and Foster spent the next quarter hour explaining why a six-hour response time to a tactical attack was unacceptable for the United States' national security. There were no questions. There were no comments. Their presentation met with stone-cold silence.

Finally, Sprague said, "Mr. President, I don't think Mr. Foster and I can contribute any more to this meeting, and I'd like permission to leave."[105]

When no one objected, the two men left the meeting.

Sprague waited until they stepped into the sunlight before he spoke. "You think anyone in there gave a damn about what we said?"

"I don't know," Foster said. "I imagine there are two possibilities. Either they change the policy—"

"—or?"

Foster's voice carried no hint of humor. "Or you and I spend the next twenty years in Leavenworth looking forward to our half hour of daily exercise."

A week later, the SAC changed its response policy. In the event of a tactical attack, more than a third of the available US aircraft would be airborne within fifteen minutes.

26

The Gaither Report

The forty-page Gaither Report was never released to the public, but it became one of the most widely publicized "secret reports" in the history of the NSC. Even before it was finished, political analyst and newspaper columnist Stewart Alsop started to question Eisenhower's massive retaliation policy in the new ICBM world. On August 26, 1957, Alsop's *New York Herald Tribune* column revealed that the President had asked Gaither to study the possibility of employing new technological means of defense against atomic attack.[106] While the Committee was attracting top-level talent, Alsop questioned whether anything solid would arise from the assignment, given the present national mood of complacency. Members of the press descended on Committee members like jackals on an abandoned carcass. Any member who proposed an ultimately rejected idea was more than happy to whine for public consumption.

A story in the December 20, 1957, issue of *The Washington Post*—a story whose accuracy was later confirmed by members of Congress—did little to calm growing national hysteria with this headline:

NATO Votes Missile Bases, Peace Try;
Secret Report Sees U.S. in Grave Peril

The article read in part:

The journalist, Chalmers Roberts, had interviewed more than twenty individuals associated with the Gaither Report and concluded: It finds America's long-term prospect one of cataclysmic peril in the face of rocketing Soviet military might and of a powerful, growing Soviet economy and technology which will bring new political propaganda and psychological assaults on freedom all around the globe.[107]

On the same day, Arthur Krock wrote a story for *The New York Times* based on a speech William Foster gave at West Point. Foster had said, "We must attempt to get away from the strange dichotomy with which we have traditionally viewed force, refusing to consider it except as a last resort, then approaching it in a crusading manner with a 'punish the bandit' view, which has been prevalent in our recent conflicts."[108]

Krock concluded the report, advocating a more aggressive defense policy, something more preemptive than preventive. Krock wrote:

> This [speech] strongly implies that the [Gaither] report to the NSC gave the most powerful support thus far in the United States to the military policy of striking an enemy before the assault he obviously is about to make on this country.[109]

ↄᴑᴐ

June 1964
DOJ Conference Room

Forde held up his hands. "How accurate were these articles?"

"They were dangerously close to the truth," Caleb said. "The Gaither Report and its progeny were the genesis for Eisenhower's kick-starting the National Strategic Target List (NSTL) and Single Integrated Option Plan (SIOP) studies.

"*Newsweek, Life* magazine, *Aviation Week, U.S. News & World Report*, and NBC TV all contributed to the national consciousness of immediate vulnerability to a Soviet surprise attack. The Joint Chiefs never doubted our nation's weakness. By October 1957, the Joint Chiefs had concluded that as many as twenty-two SAC bases would receive little or no warning of a Soviet attack. There were radar gaps that would not detect incoming bombers either below 2,000 feet or above 50,000 feet."[110]

"God help us!" Forde exclaimed.

"God couldn't help us," Caleb said. "The same lack of a warning would be true of a surprise attack carried out by missiles from Soviet submarines, assuming they had that capability. In the 1959 fiscal budget, the Navy did not request more ships. Instead, it asked for additional funds for modern anti-submarine warfare readiness. The Joint Chiefs had concluded that the most practical solution was in establishing control over the submarines prior to missile launch. In peacetime, the controls included detection, tracking, identification, hold-down tactics, and, in certain situations constituting an immediate and vital threat to the security of the United States, destruction of the submarines."[111]

"That would have been interpreted as an act of war," Forde said.

"Wouldn't have helped anything," Caleb said. "There were many itchy trigger fingers at that time. The National Intelligence Committee had vastly overestimated Soviet military capacities. The Russians had launched *Sputnik* in '57 and struck the moon with Luna rockets in '59. Khrushchev liked to posture and woof and growl. He scared the hell out of a lot of people who thought he was insane. Instead, he was calculated and highly intelligent."

Forde's face scrunched a little while he tried to assimilate the information. Caleb gave Forde a blank stare back.

Caleb thought, *I wonder if he knows about the rogue contingent in the national security establishment and the plans it developed to act—even if it cost the United States 40 million lives.*

Forde's eyes narrowed. The stunned US citizen was gone. The dedicated interrogator had returned. "Dr. Young, what did you have to do with the Gaither Report?"

Young hesitated. There were a lot of things Forde didn't know about—off-the-record meetings, first-strike plans based on the RAND Corporation's Game Theory Calculus. Caleb decided to avoid the subject.

"In 1954," Caleb went on, "NSC memo 5511 established the NESC (Net Evaluation Subcommittee), which was composed of the chairman of the Joint Chiefs of Staff (JCS), the AEC, the Interdepartmental Intelligence Conference, the Interdepartmental Committee on Internal Security, the Directors of the Office of Defense Mobilization (ODM), the Federal Civil Defense Administration (FCDA), and the CIA.[112] The NESC interpreted intelligence estimates of military and governmental agencies for the President. Director Dulles appointed me to act for him on that committee. I met several times with Robert Sprague and William Foster."

"How did the United States detect all the Soviet missile tests during 1956 and 1957?" Forde asked.

Caleb hesitated.

"I have the appropriate clearances, Dr. Young. And the possibility of a perjury charge is ever present. Remember?"

Caleb did not need to be reminded about the jeopardy to his freedom. He continued. "The missiles tested and launched from Kapustin Yar were detected by an AN/FPS-17 XW-1 General Electric radar installed on June 2, 1955, at Diyarbakir Air Station in southeast Turkey. The launches from Tyuratam were discovered approximately eight hours prior to their launch through a combination of human intelligence, communication intercepts, and signal intercepts. The eight hours of lead time to the countdown allowed us to field several reconnaissance planes that monitored both the flight and the splashdown area. From our analysis, we determined whether the Russians could mount a nuclear warhead on the missile and how accurate it might be. Everything changed on January 31, 1958."

"How?"

"*The New York Times* told everybody everything, down to the eight-hour countdown time."

Forde harrumphed. "Gotta love freedom of the press."

Caleb shook his head. "Those of us in the secrets business aren't always so enamored."

"Duly noted. Please continue."

"Well," Caleb continued, "subsequently the Russians changed the countdown time to four hours, and we lost our ability to track."

"Who were they?" Forde asked.

"I need a break," Caleb told Forde and then slipped him a note that read, "On the stairwell."

Caleb left the room first and walked out the door. He quietly went down several stairs and waited for Forde, who was peeved but found Caleb in the stairwell.

"Are you asking for the names of the people who leaked information to the press?" Caleb said in a whisper.

"No," Forde said. "The people in the national security establishment who planned a first strike."

Forde knew more than Caleb suspected. Caleb was surprised and hesitated a split second too long. "I have no personal knowledge—"

Forde's voice was soft but razor-sharp. "Cut the crap, Doctor! You are about to kiss your immunity goodbye. I get names now, or you can spend the rest of your days breaking rocks, courtesy of Uncle Sam."

"LeMay, Gates, Power, Rostow, and Admiral Anderson were the ringleaders, but you have already surmised as much," Caleb blurted out. "There were about twenty more whose names I will give you later."

"Why wait?"

"I have immunity," Caleb said, "but not protection. Some of those folks are still very powerful. I saw what happened to my parents when they crossed the wrong people in government. I have no wish to be disappeared."

"We have safe houses, Dr. Young." He sounded like a bad actor reading from a worse movie script.

"We are dealing with very determined people," Caleb whispered. "I hope you appreciate that I am the only person who can help you. If I get 86ed, you've got nothing."

"One last question before we go back in," Forde added. "What did General Thomas Power and Wozniak have to do with the Jupiter fiasco last year in April when the planet was nearly destroyed?"

So Forde knew about that operation too. "Wozniak is not his real name."

"I know that! But we have to talk with him to determine who in the National Security Establishment is capable of setting off World War III before it starts."

"Wozniak, aka Barry Schloss, is dead. He and the rest of his Green Beret team never made it out of Turkey alive. You can't continue to underestimate the Agency."

Before Forde could ask his next question, Caleb turned and headed back into the conference room.

Back in the room, Forde decided to switch gears. Maybe he finally realized this wasn't moot court and his life was on the line. "Let's finish with the Gaither Report. Review for me Secretary McElroy's testimony in front of the LBJ Senate Committee and Khrushchev's November 27, 1957, statements."

"As you know," Caleb said, "Khrushchev had openly threatened the United States with the Soviets' purported ICBM advantage. He promised . . ." Caleb paused for recollection. "I believe his exact words were 'the most devastating war ever known to mankind.' He said it would rage through Europe and Asia but that its fury would not be any less in the United States."[113]

"Did you think he was serious?"

"What I thought didn't matter," Caleb said. "I have always been a scientist, not an analyst. The Premier bragged about having the first artificial satellite and claimed the Soviets could launch ten to twenty more 'tomorrow.' He directly said there was a satellite with the United States' name on it."

Forde was implacable. He'd heard all this before.

"To answer the other part of your question, Mr. Forde, McElroy's statements to the Senate and to the press that the Soviets would have a three-to-one advantage in ICBMs by 1960 were taken out of context.[114] Stuart Symington and JFK seized on the comment to fuel their presidential aspirations. But the stage was set for dramatic changes in US defense policy that persist to this very day and will continue for years to come. Khrushchev unwittingly fired the starting pistol on an arms race. The result is a perceived first-strike window for the United States. By my calculations, the opportunity is still in play, but it is closing fast."

Forde sat up. *So now he's interested since I am talking about the end of the world,* Forde thought. "Why is it closing?"

"Technology doesn't stand still, Mr. Forde. What was optional on your car a decade ago will soon be standard equipment."

Forde snorted. "And they'll charge me for something I don't even want. I mean, what kind of man really needs an air-conditioned car? Roll down the window for goodness' sake."

Caleb shook his head. "Well, I imagine one of your ancestors moaned about the ruination of the candle industry when Mr. Edison developed the light bulb."

Forde ignored his insult. "You were explaining why the window is diminishing?"

"The Russians are not standing still any more than we are. They are developing subs with nuclear attack capacity. They are putting their ICBMs in hardened silos. They've switched to solid fuel missiles that require a shorter launch time. There is still time, but the moment the first Russian submarine slides under the waves carrying a subsurface-capable, nuclear-tipped missile, it's game over."

"When?" Forde sounded concerned for the first time in their meetings.

"No later than 1968," Caleb said.

"So we have four years."

"If that."

Forde picked up a glass of water and walked to the window. Caleb could see Forde's hand shaking. Although Forde intended to sip from his glass, he slurped and then spilled a little on his gray suit. He brushed at the water and returned to his seat, obviously agitated.

"Let's go back to the fallout from the Gaither Report," Forde reminded Caleb. "What changes were made because of that study?"

"The genie was out of the bottle," Caleb explained. "No matter how many speeches and interviews he did, President Eisenhower had lost control of the ship. The military brass was delighted, and of course, they tried not to exhibit their glee in front of Ike."

"Why were they happy?"

"They could unleash the beast. America's industrial might was available for their every weaponized fantasy. They apparently did not care about causing twice the number of World War II causalities in half an hour. They just knew they could ramp up research, development, and production of horrific, terrifying, and powerful weapons. It was a field day for the boys who like the big boom-boom."

Forde shook his head. "And a sad day for anyone interested in survival."

27

May 6, 1957 – 0800 Hours
Oval Office, the White House
Washington, DC

Eisenhower scrutinized the group on the other side of his desk—Donald Quarles, Deputy Secretary of Defense; Air Force Chief of Staff Nathan Twining; Acting Secretary of State Christian Herter; DCI Allen Dulles; Richard Bissell; and Dr. Caleb Young. The U-2 plane had recently completed its seventh overflight of the Soviet Union since the inception of the program on July 4, 1956. Those flights had provided significant information. The Soviets' claims concerning a huge fleet of intercontinental bombers were bogus. But the CIA had recently indicated to Ike the Soviets' intention to launch a missile with enough range to reach the United States. The Agency wanted to continue overflights to determine the extent of the Soviet missile threat.

"I don't need to tell any of you what's going to happen if the Soviets blockade Berlin again," Eisenhower stated. "We'll ramp up another airlift, and they will decide if they want to escalate tensions by shooting down our aircraft. They know we're overflying their territory. Hell, the *Chicago Tribune* and newspapers in London have carried stories about our reconnaissance. Very embarrassing to the Soviets."

Caleb Young raised his hand. Eisenhower acknowledged him. "Mr. President, I know more flights are a continuing risk, especially with the development of Soviet SAMs, but without these flights, we are blind regarding the number of long-range missiles the Russians have and, more importantly, their fueling time. We believe the launch sites are located along railroad tracks to facilitate the transportation of the massive amounts of required fuel."

Bissell jumped in. "Dr. Young is correct. We have four specific sites: Tyuratam, Plesetsk, Semipalatinsk, and Kapustin Yar. We believe we should overfly them."

Eisenhower then heard arguments from General Twining and Secretary of State Christian Herter in support of the continued overflights and finally agreed to let them continue with his expressed prior approval.

∞

June 1964
Office of William Forde, Esq., Chief of the Criminal Division and CIA Liaison
950 Pennsylvania Avenue, Suite 710
Washington, DC

"You have a list of the flights, I assume," Forde said.

Caleb indicated the volume and page number and flipped through the appropriate binder.

Flight #	Date	Base	Pilot	Surveillance Area	Mission Status
2013	7/4/56	Wiesbaden	Stockman	E. Ger, Poland, Minsk, Leningrad, Estonia, Latvia	Completed
2014	7/5/56	Wiesbaden	Vito	E. Ger, Warsaw, Minsk, Moscow, Estonia, Lithuania	Completed
2020	7/9/56	Wiesbaden	Knutson	E. Ger, Poland, Minsk, retrace Poland	Completed
2021	7/9/56	Wiesbaden	Overstreet	Czech, Vienna, Hungary, Lviv, Kiev, Minsk, Poland	Completed

2024	7/10/56	Wiesbaden	Dunaway	Poland, Kishinev, Kerch, Sevastopol, Simeropol, Odessa, Romania	Completed
4016	11/20/56	Adana, Tur.	Powers	Iran, Yerevan, Baku, Astara, Caucasus	Completed
4020	3/18/57	Adana, Tur.	Cherbonneaux	Azerbaijan, Armenia, Georgia	Completed
6005	6/20/57	Eielson, Alaska	Rand	Khali Yulya, Ust-Amchatsk, Kozyrevsk, Karaganskiy-Ostrov	Completed
4035	8/5/57	Lahore, Pak.	Edens	Afghanistan, Tashkent, Tyuratam, Kazalinsk, Aral Sea,	Completed
39	8/11/57	Lahore, Pak.	McMurray	Ala-Alta, Ust-Kamenogorsk, Sinkiang-(Xinjiang)	Completed
4045	8/21/57	Lahore, Pak.	Snider	Novokuznetsk, Tomsk	Completed
4048	8/21/57	Lahore, Pak.	Jones	Lake Balkhash (LB), Karaganda, Omsk, Alma. Alta	Completed
4049	8/22/57	Lahore, Pak.	Birkhead	Merket Bazar, Kuldja, Abakan, Krasnoyarsk, Kansk, Sinkiang	Completed
4050	8/22/57	Lahore, Pak.	Cherbonneaux	Lake Balkhash, Semipalatinsk, Barnaul, Prokopyevsk	Completed
4058	8/28/57	Lahore, Pak.	Jones	Dushanbe, Tashkent, Tyuratam, Kazalinsk, Aral Sea	Completed
4059	9/10/57	Adana, Tur.	Hall	Krasnovodsk, Guryev, Astrakhan, Tbilisi	Completed
6008	9/16/57	Eielson, Alaska	Baker	Kamchatka Peninsula, Milkovo	Completed

2040	10/13/57	Giebelstadt, Ger	Stockman	Norway, Finland, Murmansk, Kandalaksha	Completed
6011	3/1/58	Atsugi, Japan	Crull	Dalnerechensk, Khabarovsk, Blagoveshchensk, Belogorsk	Completed
4125	7/9/59	Peshawar, Pak.	Knutson	Tyrantrum	Completed
8005	10/6/59	Peshawar, Pak.	Robinson	Kuybyshev, Kapustin Yar, Caucasus	Completed
8009	2/5/60	Peshawar, Pak.	MacArthur	Tyrantrum, Kazan, Crimea	Completed
4155	4/9/60	Peshawar, Pak.	Ericson	Lake Balkhash, Saryshagan, Semipalatinsk, Kyzylsepe	Completed
4154	5/1/60	Peshawar, Pak.	Powers	Tyuratam, Kyshtym, Sverdlovsk	Shot Down

"That last entry is sort of the fly in the soup," Forde said.

"Indeed," Caleb said. "But we'll talk more about it later."

"Why such a big gap between the March 1, 1958, flight and the next one on July 9, 1959?"

Caleb took a breath. "The March 1, 1958, flight generated a lot of whining from the Soviets. Ike was irritated at Bissell because the stealth camouflage project failed to deceive the Soviet radar. Later in the year, relations between the United States and the Soviets only got worse. Then on November 10, Khrushchev announced a peace treaty with the GDR. He said the Allies in Berlin would have to deal with the GDR if they wanted land route access to Berlin. The State Department bungled everything."

"Little wonder," Forde said. "Dulles was about dead by then, so who was at fault?"

"Secretary Dulles was still well enough to do plenty of damage," Caleb went on. "On December 31st, the State Department sent a message to Moscow admonishing the Russians to backpedal on their plans. Norway got a message to the United States that Khrushchev could not believe the Allies would go to war over Berlin if push came to shove. On January 16, 1959, Secretary Dulles met with Anastas Mikoyan, the Deputy Premier of the Soviet Union. There was no resolution."

"Well, we are all still here, so something worked," Forde said.

"Well, the Pentagon's plans were to send a truck convoy to Berlin supported by a platoon of the U.S. Army. Basically, it was calling a bluff. If the Soviets escalated, the idea was to send a division the next time with instructions not to fire unless fired upon. General Twining met with Eisenhower, Secretary of Defense McElroy, and Dulles, who rejected the Pentagon's plans. Eisenhower preferred to send a small, armored force and prepare to evacuate civilians from West Berlin while massing troops on the border in preparation for an East German invasion."

"An awful lot of brinkmanship," Forde said.

"Boys and their games," Caleb said. "It's all very easy when someone else is going to die." He shook his head. "Anyway, General Twining believed war was inevitable and wanted to force the issue. The Administration was pretty secure because everyone in the military and in government believed we dominated the last rung of the escalation ladder—nuclear power."

"What happened?"

"Dulles could not get the British and French aboard. They wanted no part of drawing a line in the sand—a line, mind you, in the European sand. They did not want the Soviets to see anything they might interpret as inflexible."

"Understandable," Forde said. "There had been two world wars in Europe in thirty years."

"Exactly. I have no evidence, but my gut tells me they were a little irritated about America's willingness to act tough from several thousand miles away. Anyway, by April of 1959, the United States realized their European allies were not going to climb the escalation domination ladder with them. No one wanted any part of playing the last card."

"You mean pushing a button," Forde added.

"Precisely," Caleb said. "So while Khrushchev was demanding the extraction of all Allied forces from West Berlin, the pressure was mounting on Eisenhower to get eyes in the air, so to speak."

"And the flights resumed," Forde said.

"And the flights resumed."

28

June 1964
Office of William Forde, Esq., Chief of
the Criminal Division and CIA Liaison
950 Pennsylvania Avenue, Suite 710
Washington, DC

Because Forde had other duties, none apparently as pressing as grilling Caleb every day but things to do nonetheless, Caleb got the occasional morning off. In his younger years, Caleb might have spent the time noodling on some sticky physics theory or even reading philosophy. He had neither the time nor the patience for potboilers, and though he had great admiration for the work of Agatha Christie, he could usually figure out whodunnit before he was halfway through one of her novels.

He had been intrigued of late by Alistair MacLean who had produced only the excellent *The Guns of Navarone,* and a chap—an Englishman named Ian Fleming—to whom he'd been introduced by Wild Bill Donovan. Fleming's James Bond character could very easily have been based on Caleb had Bond not been urbane, suave, handsome, unfailingly successful with women, and licensed to kill. Commander Bond and Caleb did, however, share an affinity for scrambled eggs, a dish Caleb had consumed for breakfast every day of his life for as long as he could remember.

But reading was not how Caleb spent his sporadic mornings off. While he was still in relatively good shape, he spent what little time he could carve out on the basketball court at the YMCA. There is an adage, "The older I get, the better I was." It was probably truer in Caleb's case than he would care to admit, but he still approached the game in a way that made analytics more valuable than physical prowess.

He no longer won every game.

But his teams won more than they lost.

⚛

William Forde and Caleb Young's meetings—or interrogations as Caleb called them—resumed the next day. Forde spoke first, continuing where they had left off. "Your conclusion for a US window of opportunity for a knockout blow does not square with the Harmon Report, the report from the Weapons Systems Evaluation Group, or the seven-volume Net Evaluation Subcommittee Reports for SIOP-62 and SIOP-63. None of these have ever concluded that the United States had a clean first-strike window. I believe the most optimistic of those reports concluded that at least 10 million Americans would die even if everything went according to plan on a preventative or even preemptive strike by the United States."

"None of those analysts had the information I had," Caleb claimed. "I got my data from Oleg Penkovsky at the peace conferences. He was very forthcoming. The Soviets were suffering from a complete lack of command-and-control coordination of both their bombers and their bombs. The United States' so-called experts did not consider utilization of the carrier-based A-3Ds, A-5s, the English Avro, or the Thor and Jupiter missiles. They did not account for how our B-52s and B-47s on alert and based in Europe and the Middle East deprived the Soviets of sufficient time to respond in any meaningful manner to even a preventive attack. Moreover, Mr. Forde, they missed the most crucial point—the woeful lack of preparedness of the Soviet offensive capabilities."

"You sound awfully sure of yourself—as a minority of one."

"I am not sure of myself . . . I am absolutely right," Caleb confidently claimed. "Soviet ICBMs were a non-factor. They could not so much as clear their pads before our missiles and bombers had destroyed all the Soviet above-ground launch facilities. For the period we're discussing, the Soviets lacked hardened silos for their ICBMs. Thanks to the U-2 flights, we knew the location of every Soviet long-range bomber air base. When the Soviets got lucky and picked up our flights, they scrambled interceptors. They might as well have hung out a sign that read 'Our Planes Are Here.'"

"I assume you helped calculate the bases' locations."

"Child's play, sir. It's basic math based on aircraft capacities for distance, how long they were in the air, how long they took to appear, and other factors. Even an attorney could do the calculations."

Forde said something, but of course it was too muffled for Caleb to hear.

Caleb realized his insult and said, "I really did not mean to insult you, sir. It was unnecessary."

"No, I apologize," Forde said. "I was reacting—badly. I did not intend to offend."

"None taken." Caleb chuckled inside that Forde had just apologized for offending *him*.

"Now, once everything is blown up by General LeMay," Caleb carried on, "what do the Soviets have left? Bison and Bear bombers. Both planes suffer from readiness problems. The Bison is a one-way craft, simply a redesign of our B-29. They could not deliver bombs safely in the Korean War. They had made no significant progress. And yes, before you ask, I intentionally gave false and misleading information to the NSC from 1953 to 1963 about potential damage from Soviet bombers."

"What about the Soviet ballistic missile submarines and our NATO allies?" Forde asked.

"The submarines had to surface, and the range of the RF-11s and other ballistic missiles was minimal. Their threat was potential, not probable. Our ASW abilities, which included the Sound Surveillance System (SOSUS) line, made it very difficult for any SSBM to get close enough to do any damage to the United States through mid-1963. LeMay and his coterie didn't care about NATO casualties. They were simply collateral damage, so the hardened silos for the IRBMs and MRBMs SS-4 and SS-5 were not a consideration because they didn't threaten the United States."

"You gambled with millions of American lives and were willing to kill about 300 million people in Russia, China, and Europe! Why didn't you disclose the potential plot?"

"Mr. Forde, I do not think you understand."

"I do not, Dr. Young."

"Well, I've done everything I can but draw you a diagram. Perhaps we will try that later."

Forde offered up a very audible, not muffled expletive.

"You do have a temper."

"You are an inveterate ass, Doctor."

"So I have been told, even by those whose opinions matter to me. Dr. Einstein once called me the most arrogant adolescent on the planet. I considered it the supreme compliment. But enough about me. Let's get back to the U-2 flights. I need to go over Operation Soft Touch and cover the last four flights so you will have better insight into my analysis and what I had to do to influence the Net Evaluation Subcommittee.

"The report had to indicate that the United States would suffer significant casualties and degradation of the strategic nuclear forces. Otherwise there would have been a nearly irresistible push toward a preemptive strike based on NESC reports. In reality, ExCom, Kennedy's Executive Committee during the Cuban Missile Crisis, almost did it anyway. They almost got Kennedy to order an assault on Cuba that would have ended in a full-scale nuclear war in which the United States would have prevailed. But, as Ike said, what do you do with a smoldering radioactive Russia? As you know, JFK stopped them. His brother Bobby was no help, and the BS he's putting out in his book about how he brokered peace is beyond ridiculous. He was a bigger warmonger than LeMay during those meetings."

"So you lied to every President you worked for?"

"I protected Presidents from their darker angels and the non-angelic people who surrounded them. Ike turned down the Pentagon and wouldn't even consider a preventive strike during his last couple of years in office. President Kennedy never considered any sort of strike except against China's nuclear facilities. All JFK and I had to do was watch the generals and stop them from ginning up a situation for a preventive war—something they most assuredly tried both during the Cuban Missile situation and the Turkey fiasco. Eisenhower, military whiz that he was, might have hit the Russians if he'd thought the situation was right, but for most of his presidency, he never realized the opportunity existed."

"So you admit to lying."

"No, Mr. Forde, because I didn't have to lie. Not to them. Just to the Joint Chiefs and the DCI. Let's go back to the U-2 flights. They set foreign policy, dictated defense budgets, and instilled fear in the Soviet leadership.

"You do realize that in September 1958, Ike was ready to nuke China over Quemoy and Matsu, two tiny islands a couple miles off the Chinese mainland. You also must realize that just last year Kennedy tried to get Khrushchev to agree to nuke the Chinese nuclear development sites to prevent the proliferation of nuclear weapons. Has anything I've said about the utter worldwide destructive force of nuclear weapons sunk in? Mr. Forde, let me be crystal clear. Nuclear war cannot be contained, and it will be horrific. No one here in America is ready for anything like what Europe and Asia went through during World War II. We live in a theoretical fantasy world where our generals talk in megatons but have little if any idea of the global consequences of the damage that even a limited nuclear war will cause."

Forde frowned. "So why did you and Kaysen draw up your plan?"

"If war came, it was our only hope for the survival of the human species. I'm moving on."

∽

March 11, 1957 – 0833 Hours
CIA Headquarters
Langley, Virginia

Henry Lowenhaupt had worked with Caleb Young for a long time. He didn't particularly like the scientist. People who made other people feel stupid did little for Henry, but as he thought about it, most everyone looked stupid compared to this physicist.

"Dr. Young." Despite their long association, Lowenhaupt always used Young's title. "I have talked with all the people on your list who worked at Oakridge on the Manhattan Project. I've looked at the old maps we have from World War II and even had some of our agents interview refugees who worked on huge projects in the Soviet Union. I have reached some definite ideas regarding the production sites for Russian uranium. The sites must be near a dam because they require a massive amount of hydroelectric power."

Caleb nodded the way someone does when they see a friend's child doing something mundane—like walking. Everyone else goes nuts, so it is required to be polite and smile or, in this case, nod. "Thank you for your diligence, Henry. I will take your assessments to Bissell and the Director and see if I can convince them to take this map to the President."

Lowenhaupt's research had taken a lot of effort. It followed leads regarding seven German scientists captured by the Soviet Union near the end of World War II. He had correctly discerned that the Soviet atomic program was under the direction of Colonel-General Avraami Pavlovich Zavenyagin, the Chief of the Ninth Directorate MVD in 1947. The lead German scientist was Gustav Hertz, a Nobel Prize winner in Physics and head of the Siemens-Halske Laboratory in 1934. Through travel schedules and mail intercepts in Berlin, Lowenhaupt had reliably predicted the location of most of the Soviet nuclear efforts. His word held sway with Director Dulles who was able to get authorization for a series of U-2 overflights called Operation Soft Touch to confirm Lowenhaupt's assessment.

There had been nine U-2 flights from Peshawar Airfield in Lahore, Pakistan, since August 1957. They revealed nuclear facilities at Tomsk, Novosibirsk, Krasnoyarsk, and an atomic weapons test site at Semipalatinsk. But the most important strategic find was made early on during Flight 4035.

On August 5, Eugene "Buster" Eden was following the Moscow-Tashkent railroad. He obliquely photographed an ICBM test site at Tyuratam for the first time. The last of the nine Operation Soft Touch overflights, mission 4058 flown by Edwin K. Jones on August 28, 1957, revealed only one launch pad. A later follow-up mission by Marty Knutson on July 9, 1959, revealed two more.

Khrushchev's boast of 250 ICBMs was baloney.

And the West knew it.

ICBM development proved problematic for the Soviets. They changed the focus to intermediate and medium-range missiles, thereby making them more susceptible to a US first strike. The only credible ICBM facility was vulnerable, above ground. As late as 1963, it had only a quartet of ICBMs. The rest of the U-2 flights proved beyond a doubt that there was no missile gap, just as there had never been a bomber gap.

So much for the Premier's bluff and bluster.

∽

June 1964
Office of William Forde, Esq., Chief of the Criminal Division and CIA Liaison
950 Pennsylvania Avenue, Suite 710
Washington, DC

"Mr. Forde, as you will see when we get into the details with the NSTL and the SIOP documents, any hopes the Soviet Union had for a retaliatory strike in 1963 lay strictly with their five active Hotel Class II Project 658 submarines." Caleb was giving Forde a lot of details—details that Forde apparently didn't understand, but he went on. "They were nuclear powered and easy to follow because they made more noise than diesel electric vessels. The Project 658s were equipped with D-4 launchers and three R-21 missiles with a range of 650 miles. Each warhead was an 800 kiloton warhead and could be launched while submerged. Again, the ease of tracking made them pretty much sitting ducks—or whales in this case. But the Russians were very focused on improving their submarines' stealth capabilities, and my estimate is that by 1968 they will have done so, closing our first-strike window for good. There are other reasons the window is closing, but that is the main one, and we don't need any more facts on that." Caleb allowed himself a rare smile.

Forde tried to hide his smile by sipping from a water glass, but Caleb saw it. Forde circled his index finger to indicate that Caleb should move along.

"All the worry about Russian subs hitting SAC bases was not realistic. The fear was mongered by the Air Force that wanted an overwhelming first-strike capability. Everything is there in the last notebook."

Forde looked like a kid who'd just been assigned additional homework. "The last volume is your plan for a first strike, correct?" Forde asked.

Caleb nodded.

"If you were so opposed to the idea, Dr. Young, why did you go into such detail concerning how a first strike could be carried out successfully?"

Caleb winced. Forde, thinking Caleb must have a headache, leaned over and asked, "Are you okay?"

"I am," Caleb said. "I'm just weary of people who do not understand that I never do anything . . . uh . . ."

Forde finished his sentence for him. ". . . half-assed?"

"Yes," Caleb said, grateful Forde had allowed him to avoid the crude statement he had been on the brink of uttering.

"Besides, when the next opportunity comes around, people like you and Bobby Kennedy, once he comes to his senses, will be around to stop it. I will not be here to help. The generals may well convince President Johnson about the advisability of a first strike, but by the time they do, it will not be feasible, as my outline will demonstrate beyond any doubt."

"Why's that?"

"The Soviets are catching up. I estimate the window of our advantage will close in forty-eight months, if not sooner. After that, if we launch, they launch, and it will be a disaster. If nothing else, a mutual mistake of such magnitude will destroy our atmosphere by changing the ozone layer in a chemical reaction."

Forde looked skeptical. "You don't know that for sure."

"Well, true—at least in a scientific fact sense. My theory depends on burst height and megatonnage. But in four years, any exchange will involve massive explosive capacity and high radiation yield. Let's look at the last four U-2 flights over Russia."

Forde shook his head. "You change directions quicker than Willie Galimore."

"As you know, I am more of a basketball person, but I know who the Wisp is."

Forde looked surprised.

"I may be what you refer to as a pencil-headed geek, but I am very well rounded when it comes to a number of current events."

"Oh yeah?" Forde asked.

"Yes."

"What's the number-one song?"

Caleb didn't hesitate. "I imagine you are referring to the Cash Box rankings. On May 23rd, it was 'Love Me Do' by the Beatles. Mary Wells supplanted them on May 30 with 'My Guy,' but for the last two weeks, the charts have been ruled by a most exorable tune, 'Chapel of Love' by the Dixie Cups."

"Again, you surprise me, Dr. Young. But what's wrong with 'Chapel of Love'?"

"Nothing," Caleb said, "if you like vapid, silly songs about going to the chapel and getting married." He paused and steepled his fingers. "Mark my word, the Dixie Cups will be a bug on the windshield of the bus carrying those young men from Liverpool who will perhaps be the most singular musical force of the next decade."

Forde jolted, almost tipping over his glass of water. "With their floppy hair and 'yeah, yeah, yeah'? You really think so?"

"I do," Caleb said with confidence. "There is a rawness in their music that does not exist in a lot of other popular acts. Oh, you will have the occasional snappy or sappy tune that will rise like a skyrocket, make a big noise, and then dissipate, but those lads from across the pond are here to stay."

Forde shook his head. "Well, I guess it's all right as long as those damn hairstyles go away."

Caleb laughed—out loud.

"What's so funny?" Forde asked.

"Mr. Forde, in a few years, I imagine you will look back with longing on those 'damn hairstyles' you currently find so offensive."

"Not damn likely," Forde said.

"You sound like the people who cursed the iron horse, the electric light, and two-piece underwear."

Now Forde grinned. "Okay, back to work."

29

June 1964
Office of William Forde, Esq., Chief of
the Criminal Division and CIA Liaison
950 Pennsylvania Avenue, Suite 710
Washington, DC

"We still haven't talked about it," Forde said.

"I am well aware," Caleb said. "And we will not address the assassination of President Kennedy until I believe it is in proper sequence."

"You have a hard time talking about it, don't you?" Forde asked.

"I do not believe very many people list it among their favorite conversational topics."

Forde looked a little lost for a moment, so Caleb decided to move on. "Let's consider the last four U-2 flights. They were very important."

Forde didn't respond and made no twirling gesture with his finger. Caleb didn't care and kept going.

"We've discussed Khrushchev's braggadocio," Caleb said. "Upon his return to Moscow from the United States in late 1959, he continued to embellish Soviet military capabilities. In November of that year, he claimed that the Soviets had a stockpile of atomic and hydrogen weapons sufficient to wipe out all potential enemies from the face of the Earth. His exact words were, 'In one year, 250 rockets with hydrogen warheads came off the assembly line in the factory we visited.'"[115]

"Impressive," Forde said.

"Total fertilizer," Caleb said. "Despite Eisenhower's policy toward the British during the Suez Crisis, they agreed to take some of the heat off him by flying the next two U-2 flights. On October 6, 1959, Robbie Robinson flew operation High Wire out of Peshawar, which covered Kuybyshev, Engels Airfield at Saratov, and the Kapustin Yar Missile Test Range before landing at Adana Air Base in Turkey. Robinson's mission was a success because it located a squadron of long-range bombers at the Engels Airfield. The Air Force promptly added that airfield to its target list. But the flight did not discover any new missile sites, and the debate about the number of Soviet missiles continued to gain steam. Congress grilled Director Dulles about his low estimates, but he could not reveal the overflights. His embarrassment made him more determined to get authorization to follow the railroad tracks."[116]

"He assumed the rocket fuel was coming in by rail?" Forde asked.

"Yes. Eisenhower approved another British overflight for February 1960. The intent was to settle the missile gap controversy by following the most likely railroad tracks. On February 5, 1960, British Squadron Leader John MacArthur took off from Peshawar, Pakistan, overflew the Tyuratam Missile Test Range, and then headed northwest to Kazan, Russia, where he photographed a new Soviet bomber called the Tu-98 Backfin. It turned out to be a bust for the Soviets because it lacked intercontinental range.

"MacArthur then turned south and photographed long stretches of the Soviet rail network, but the pictures did not reveal a single missile site. Dulles pushed for more overflights since the Air Force still insisted there were as many as a hundred Soviet ICBMs. Even so, experts at the Air Technical Intelligence Center (ATIC) released a study in which they highlighted the growing dangers from continued overflights based on advancements in Soviet surface-to-air missile technology. You can see the conclusion in Appendix LX."

Caleb gave Forde some time to find the appendix in the binder. Part of it read:

> The greatest threat to the U-2 is the Soviet SAM, although the ATIC (Air Technical Intelligence Committee Wright-Patterson AFB) analysis concedes a remote possibility that the SAM may be less effective than estimated, their present evaluation is that the SAM-2 (Guideline) has a high probability of successful intercept at 70,000 feet providing that detection is made in sufficient time to alert the site.[117]

"Sounds like they were warned," Forde said.

"They were," Caleb said. "Still, the payoff from the previous two flights had been huge. The next overflight was scheduled for April 10, 1960. And that is where I participated in a major miscalculation."

"Can't say it, can you, Doctor?"

"Say what?"

"Can't say you were wrong."

Caleb took a sip of water and adjusted his bow tie. "I am a scientist, Mr. Forde. I interpret data and seek answers. I pursue theories, many of which prove invalid. Being wrong never bothers me because I am in relentless pursuit of being right."

Forde waved one hand in the air as if to say it didn't matter.

"Whether we knew or not, I cannot recall," Caleb continued, "but neither Bissell nor I realized the Soviets had not protested the latest two flights by British pilots."

"Baiting you, weren't they?" Forde said.

"Brave men risked their lives, Mr. Forde. Smugness is not an appropriate attitude here. This is not a fencing match."

Forde bit his lip. "My apologies. But—"

"But that's exactly right," Caleb interrupted. "They set the trap, and we wandered in like babes in the woods."

❦

April 10, 1960 – 0142 Hours
12th Air Defense Army – Tashkent HQ
24th and 37th Corps of the PVO

"Target acquired on a heading of 340 degrees north-northwest at 74,000 feet," announced Lieutenant Karkov. "Alert the missile batteries."

"The target is moving outside our range," added Colonel Kartika. "The next battery is not on alert. Continue to track, and send the report to the 2nd, 4th, and 19th Air Defense Armies."

"Colonel, begging your pardon, there is no need to alert the 19th unless the American turns south."

Kartika answered quickly. "Our information indicates the mission is intended to cover Tyuratam and Saryshagan. If we shoot and miss, the Americans will know we have the ability to bring down their planes. They will be alerted, and General Biryuzov will send us back to missile school . . . or to Siberia."

No missiles were launched. Khrushchev was furious.

❦

April 23, 1960 – 0736 Hours
Senate Building, the Kremlin

Khrushchev had summoned Rodion Malinovsky, the Minister of Defense; Konstantin Vershinin, Commander in Chief of the Soviet Air Force; and Sergey Biryuzov, Commander in Chief of the Air Defense Forces to the Kremlin and demanded an explanation.

"We had three days' notice of the flight via COMINTs!" Khrushchev shouted. His bald dome glowed as red as the hammer and sickle flag behind his desk. "I feel shame for the entire country. The Americans are making fools of us. We are the laughingstock of the entire world. We have provided you with superior rockets. They can reach an altitude of 25 kilometers, and yet you cannot shoot down a plane flying at a subsonic speed. What is the problem? Are you stupid or simply incompetent?"

Sweat trickled down Biryuzov's spine, but he knew that showing fear meant a one-way ticket to oblivion. "Premier Khrushchev," he said, "the main staff of the Air Defense Forces is investigating the reasons for the failure of the Air and Defense Forces to shoot down the intruder. Colonel Alexander Orlov is here today to give us a full report on why the American intruder was not shot down even though he occupied our air space for over six hours."[118]

Orlov knew better than to push back, but he had a brief image of slicing Biryuzov's eyelids off with a razor. "Premier Khrushchev," Orlov said, "thank you to my colleague for the opportunity to be here today." He again fought the temptation to stick his foot in Biryuzov's face. "We have serious shortcomings in air combat training, in command and control of air defense and Air Force personnel, and in weapons systems. Many omissions have been discovered in the operation of advanced radio equipment. In particular, information related to this reconnaissance activity was acquired by our communication interception facilities in the Trans Caucasus division several days before it transpired, but the information was not reported to the command element. All incompetent officers and technicians have been replaced with instructors for the time being who will remain on duty until the intruders are shot down. We now have over 400 SAM sites active with our newest C-75s. We will have 600 by the end of 1963."

Khrushchev glowered. "You are dismissed, Colonel. But before you leave, be very clear on this. If the next American flight passes over our beloved nation unscathed, the next changes will be made at a much higher level."

Orlov opened the door and then froze with Khrushchev's next words.

"And the changes will not be pleasant for those involved."

30

May 1, 1960 – 0420 Hours
Peshawar Airfield, Badaber, Pakistan

Colonel William Shelton, Detachment Chief in Badaber, finally received the much awaited "go" signal. Shelton left his van and ran across the runway. He raised his right thumb.

From inside the U-2, Francis Gary Powers acknowledged and began to taxi. Powers was the Agency's most experienced pilot. He'd flown twenty-seven missions. The Article 360 he was piloting was equipped with the latest iteration of the J75-P-13B Pratt and Whitney engine and could cruise at well over 74,000 feet. But there were two significant, negative aspects.

First, mission 4154 (Operation Touchdown) was the most ambitious incursion over Soviet air space yet attempted.

Second, the go signal had come in via an unguarded Morse code communication. A Boy Scout troop from Topeka could have intercepted the message.

∽

Powers cleared the Hindu Kush range of the Himalayas and passed into the southern USSR without incident. He was scheduled for a 2,900-mile trek over Soviet territory from Dushanbe and the Aral Sea all the way to Murmansk on the Barents Sea. He was targeting the ICBM Center at Tyuratam, along with other Soviet facilities. His terminus was Bodo, Norway.

Soviet radar had picked him up while he was still in Afghanistan. Air defense systems across the nation went on high alert. All other aircraft, civilian and military, were immediately grounded. Biryuzov sat behind a large table in the Kremlin facing a map of the entire Soviet Union and watched as a minion moved a model replica of the U-2 across a screen. Colonel General Pavel Kuleshov, in charge of anti-aircraft artillery and missiles, sat to his right. On the other side was Yevgeny Savitsky, Marshal of Aviation. They knew Khrushchev had been alerted by Rodion Malinovsky, the Minister of Defense, at 0600 hours when the spy plane was more than 150 miles inside Soviet air space.

Every man knew that his career—and perhaps his life— was on the line.

Malinovsky had told Khrushchev, "We have a very good possibility of shooting the intruder down if our missile forces are not gawking at crows!"

Unamused, Khrushchev finished his breakfast and called Biryuzov. After the fourth communication, Biryuzov told the Premier that Sukhoi Su-9 and Yak-26 intercept planes were being scrambled. "If all else fails," he said, "we will ram the intruder."

Captain Igor Mentyukov, based at Sverdlovsk, was the only Su-9 pilot on Powers' route. He was placed in a weaponless plane to maximize altitude and given ramming orders. He intercepted Powers 250 kilometers south of Sverdlovsk and, despite plaintive cries from the radar control tower, feigned an inability to see the U-2 and broke off the engagement after buzzing Powers' U-2 in hopes the prop wash would tear the flimsy wings from the plane. He heard the radar operator screaming, "There he is, straight ahead of you! You must see him; you are almost on top of him!"

Once the Ben Hur tactic failed, the Soviets' last best hope lay in the six SAM sites at Sverdlovsk.

∞

"Shit!"

Powers saw the autopilot light blinking. He was 1,300 miles into Soviet territory. This was not the place for a problem. He switched to manual control. Had he beat a hasty retreat, no one would have thought twice. Everyone respected his ability and his courage. But he reasoned he had 1,600 miles ahead of him with clear skies and 1,300 miles behind him with bad weather closing in, so it made more sense to move forward. He had also been briefed on how important it was to photograph Sverdlovsk.

As Powers approached Sverdlovsk from the southeast, he noted an airfield that was not on the map he had been given. He executed a 90-degree turn to photograph the southwestern part of the city. He heard a thump and felt a vibration at the rear of his craft. The plane lurched forward, and the sky glowed orange for a few seconds.

Powers thought he'd been hit, but the instruments read normal, and the plane seemed to be operating fine. The right wing dropped for a moment. Powers corrected.

"Okay," he said, "it was a close call. All good."

Then all hell broke loose.

The nose dipped. When Powers pulled back, the dive continued. The plane shook, and the wings detached. The fuselage began to spiral like a drill bit. His flight suit had inflated because of a loss of cabin pressure. He was a stuffed sausage trapped in a spinning tube. He turned on his emergency oxygen supply, pulled one leg under him, and then the other. He disconnected his safety harness and hit the eject button.[119]

He flew out of the cockpit at 34,000 feet but was still tethered to the plane by his oxygen hose. He managed to sever the hose at about 20,000 feet; the parachute deployed at 15,000 feet.

Powers landed about 50 feet from a farmer who was plowing his field. When the police arrived, they took him to the KGB office in Sverdlovsk.[120]

∽

After five days of ridiculous attempts to deny spying—"a weather recon plane blown off course"—President Eisenhower admitted the truth. And any hope of slowing the arms race sat in a corner and suffocated.

31

June 1964
Office of William Forde, Esq., Chief of
the Criminal Division and CIA Liaison
950 Pennsylvania Avenue, Suite 710
Washington, DC

"Khrushchev was more than angry with the United States for flying a plane over the Soviet Union," Caleb told Forde. Then he read from his binder what Khrushchev said.

> In the first place, denounce the impermissible provocative actions of the American Air Force with regard to the Soviet Union and, in the second place, refrain from continuing such actions and such a policy against the USSR in the future. It goes without saying that in this event the government of the United States cannot fail to call strictly to account those directly responsible for the deliberate violation of the state frontiers of the USSR by American planes, and Eisenhower should express regret.[121]

Forde shook his head. "So ol' Nikita was a little worked up, huh?"

"That's what he said at the Paris Summit on May 16, 1960," Caleb said. "And it didn't get any better. When Ike began his remarks, Khrushchev interrupted." Caleb looked at his notes and read what Khrushchev had said.

> How can agreement be sought on the various issues which require a settlement with the object of reducing tension and eliminating suspicion and distrust between the states, when the government of one of the great powers bluntly declares that its policy is intrusion into the territory of another great power for purposes of espionage and sabotage and consequently, the aggravation of tension in relations between the powers

is escalated? It is obvious that the proclamation of such a policy, which can be carried out only when countries are in a state of war, dooms the summit meeting to complete failure in advance.[122]

Forde shook his head and asked, "Anyone try to help Ike out?"

"Charles de Gaulle did," Caleb said. "He explained how everyone spies a little and then asked what Soviet satellites were doing over their land."

Forde laughed at the understatement.

"Then Khrushchev said, 'As God is my witness, my hands are clean, and my soul is pure. Those satellites have no cameras.'"[123]

"Interesting comment from a . . . a . . . godless commie, isn't it?"

"At the very least," Caleb said. "The summit was a disaster. Khrushchev uninvited Eisenhower to Moscow, saying the Russian people would not tolerate his presence. Ike never recovered. He stumbled through the remainder of his term and probably hurt Nixon's election chances."

"Well, Powers was released, right?" Forde asked.

"One year, nine months, and ten days later, he came home to a chilly reception. He hadn't been able to hit the self-destruct button and had not taken his suicide pill."

"Think he was a coward?"

"No, I do not think the facts lead to such a conclusion. Why die for something everyone already knows about? He was downed through the fault of others—me included. We did not acknowledge that the Russians could hit his plane. We were arrogant enough to believe we had built the ultimate spy machine. The only solace we could take in the entire sorry episode was that the Russians shot down one of their own planes in the process."

"They did?"

"Oh yes," Caleb said. "One of their Su-9s hit a MiG-17 that was trying to get to Powers but could not climb high enough. It blew it right out of the sky."

"Well, I guess that's something," Forde said.

"It is, but it's not much comfort to some unnamed Russian's widow and fatherless children."

On that somber note, Forde brought the session to a close.

Epilogue

November 22, 1963 – 1343 Hours
YMCA, Washington, DC

Caleb was still one of the better players, but now he didn't dominate. Even a thorough understanding of angles, acceleration, and all the other aspects of physics that had helped him develop into a masterful basketball player were not enough to overcome the sheer physical superiority of youth.

The quality of the lunchtime players had improved over the years. More and more of them had played serious college ball, and even the ones who had not were still two decades Caleb's junior. The longer the games went, the more Caleb's flagging stamina became evident.

Where once he had outlasted and outthought everyone on the floor, he now found himself a half-step slow and seemingly a little low on giddy-up. His pump fakes were not as convincing, his set shot was less dependable in later games, and his legs were uncharacteristically wobbly after three or four rotations. Instead of staying on the floor with the winners for the entire time, more often than ever before he found himself waiting for a game to finish, sitting on the floor with the other losers as "the next up."

But what really bothered him was that it didn't bother him. His killer competitiveness had been replaced by the simple enjoyment of getting a little exercise—a momentary break in the daily grind of political intrigue and career survival. Compared to the deadly game of nuclear brinksmanship he witnessed every day, winning on the hardwood seemed petty . . . inconsequential. As his father would have said, "existentially insignificant."

"Hey, Doc, we're up!"

Caleb looked at his teammates, stood, and stretched his quads. He had to do a lot more of that these days. Someone flipped him a ball. He dribbled it a few times and passed it to himself off the wall before trotting out to the free throw line to determine which team would get first possession.

Caleb set his feet and locked his eyes on the rim. He drew the ball back and let it fly.

The door to the gym burst open. A red-faced woman stood in the opening. Mascara raccooned her eyes. Her lipstick was smeared. She was screaming.

"President Kennedy's been shot!"

AUTHOR'S COMMENTARY ON NUCLEAR WEAPONS
A PUGWASH NUCLEAR PRIMER

In the well-known novel *Moby Dick,* Herman Melville cleverly intertwines into his fictional narrative some interesting, factual information about whales. He devotes an entire chapter and a total of about 100 pages to cetology—the study of whales. I want to do the same—to give you some important information, not about whales but about nuclear weapons, the running theme of this book and the others in the *First Strike* series. If you take away nothing else from this series, I hope you learn more about and seriously consider the incredibly destructive power of nuclear weapons—the atomic bomb, the hydrogen bomb, fusion bombs—and their inevitable proliferation and potential ability to destroy the world as we know it.

After the United States exploded the first fusion-hydrogen bomb (*Ivy Mike*) on November 1, 1952, and the Soviets followed suit with *Joe 4* on August 12, 1953, India's Prime Minister Jawaharlal Nehru proposed a global halt to nuclear weapons testing. A year later, Bertrand Russell called on scientists to meet and assess where we were headed and how we could create peaceful solutions to world conflicts. Eleven brilliant scientists and thinkers signed Russell's manifesto. In 1957, the first meeting was held at Pugwash, Nova Scotia, Canada. It was called the Pugwash Conference and still takes place today. It is clear that mainstream scientists like those at the Pugwash Conferences over the decades sense the potential end of civilization due to the immense destructive power of fusion bombs as opposed to fission bombs.

Scientists, politicians, and most military leaders today recognize the possibility of weapons disrupting the fragility and interdependence of our ecosystems. Anthropogenic activity—environmental change caused by humans—has resulted in damage to ecosystems such as our rainforests and coral reefs.

Nuclear weapons testing is also affecting our environment. Many efforts have been made to control atmospheric testing of nuclear weapons, including the August 5, 1963, Limited Test Ban Treaty, SALT I, SALT II, and numerous other diplomatic efforts. Recent failures include the arms race triggered by George W. Bush's withdrawal from the Anti-Ballistic Missile Treaty and Vladimir Putin's repudiation of the New START Treaty on February 21, 2023.

A Nuclear Primer

Dynamite vs. TNT

The first nuclear weapon was tested in the Western United States on July 16, 1945. The explosive force of that weapon was measured in a chemical equivalent of thousands (or millions) of tons of TNT, short for trinitrotoluene—chemical makeup C7-H5-N3-O6 or, alternatively, C6 H2 (NO2) CH3. Tritonal, a mixture of 80 percent TNT and 20 percent aluminum powder, is used in several types of ordinances such as conventional air-dropped bombs and is approximately 18 percent more powerful than TNT alone.

Dynamite is a combination of nitroglycerin and kieselguhr, a porous, absorbent sand-like diatomaceous earth. Combined with nitroglycerin, it forms a paste that can be shaped into rods and inserted into drilling holes. A stick of dynamite is about 8" long and 1.25" in diameter and weighs about 190 grams. A single stick of dynamite produces approximately 1 MJ (million joules) of energy. A similar sized stick of TNT would produce about .7983 MJ, about 80 percent as forceful as dynamite. Twenty kilotons of TNT equals about 16,000 tons of dynamite.

A metric ton is the equivalent of 2,204 pounds. There are 5,263 sticks of dynamite per metric ton. A 1 kiloton weapon represents the dynamic force of 5,263,000 sticks of dynamite. A megaton bomb equals 5,263,000,000 sticks.

Ironically, dynamite is what Alfred Nobel used as the primary funding source for the prizes so highly sought in the areas of physics, literature, and, of course, world peace.

The Hiroshima Bomb

Shortly after the test, a uranium-based nuclear bomb called *Little Boy* was dropped on Hiroshima, Japan. It killed 80,000 people instantly in the 12.6 km blast area. Over the next decade, another 100,000 to 110,000 died from the after-effects. They did not die "in peaceful repose." Many succumbed to third-degree burns caused by thermal radiation. They had been as far as 8 km from the blast's epicenter.

The bomb weighed 4,400 kg and contained 64 kg of highly enriched uranium. It was detonated at an altitude of 600 meters to maximize the effective blast radius.

The Nagasaki Bomb

On August 9, 1945, *Fat Man,* implosion model plutonium 20 kt bomb weighing 4,672 kg and yielding 84TJ of energy, was exploded at a height of 503 meters above Nagasaki, Japan. It produced a mushroom cloud that reached an altitude of 18,288 meters and distributed energy in roughly the same pattern as the Hiroshima bomb. But because of the geography, the explosion flattened only 6.7 sq km, far less area than the less-powerful Hiroshima bomb. The bomb killed 70,000 instantly and another 30,000–40,000 across the years.

Acronyms

ARDC – Air Research Development Committee
CIA – Central Intelligence Agency
CIC – Combat Information Center
CCF – Chinese Communist Forces
CCP – Chinese Communist Party
CIG – Central Intelligence Group
CMEA – Council for Mutual Economic Assistance
DOJ – Department of Justice
DDP – Deputy Director for Plans (CIA)
DC – District of Columbia
FBG – Fighter Bomber Group
FBI – Federal Bureau of Investigation
FDR – Franklin Delano Roosevelt
FEAF – Far East Air Force
FIW – Fighter Interceptor Wing
FSW-0 – first strike weapon zero response
G-2 – Army intelligence at division level or higher
GIAD – Guards Fighter Aviation Division (Soviet)
GIAP – Guards Fighter Aviation Regiment (Soviet)
GRU – Foreign Military Intelligence Agency (Soviet)
IAD – Fighter Aviation Division (Soviet)
IAS – Institute for Advanced Study (Princeton)
ICBM – intercontinental ballistic missile
IRBM – intermediate-range ballistic missile
J – joule – unit of energy (equals one newton-meter or one
   watt-second)
JCS – Joint Chiefs of Staff
JIC – Joint Intelligence Committee
JSPG – Joint Strategic Plans Group
JWPC – Joint War Plans Committee
KGB – main security agency for the Soviet Union
KPA – Korean People's Army
KPD – Communist Party of Germany

MAUD Committee – British scientific group on development
of the atomic bomb

Me-262 – Messerschmitt World War II German jet used by
Soviets and the United States to create MiG-15 and
F-86 Sabre

MeV– mega electron volt – 1,000,000 electron volts

MGB – security agency for the Soviet Union – secret police
counterintelligence

MI-6 – Military Intelligence Section 6 (Secret Intelligence
Service, United Kingdom)

MiG – Mikoyan–Gurevich – jet fighter manufacturer for
Soviet Union

MVD – Ministry of Internal Affairs (Soviet)

NATO – North Atlantic Treaty Organization

NIA – National Intelligence Authority (US) – monitored the
Central Intelligence Group (CIG)

NDRC – National Defense Research Committee

NKVD – People's Commissariat of Internal Affairs (Soviet) –
dissolved on March 15, 1946, but survived by several
subagencies such as the MVD, a forerunner of the KGB

NSA – National Security Agency (US) – makes and processes
intelligence intercepts

NSAM – National Security Action Memorandum

NSTL – National Strategic Target List

ONI – Office of Naval Intelligence

ORE – Office of Reports and Estimates (CIA)

OSRD – Office of Scientific Research and Development (US)

OSS – Office of Strategic Services (US)

Pu-239 – plutonium isotope used in Fat Man bomb dropped
on Nagasaki

Pu-240 – plutonium isotope undesirable for scission bomb due
to premature detonation

PAL – permissive action link

SAT – Scholastic Aptitude Test

SI – Select Intelligence Division (of the OSS)

SLBM – submarine-launched ballistic missile

SS – *Schutzstaffeln* – Nazi paramilitary organization (name
    means protective echelon)
SS-4 – NATO's reporting name for R-12 Dvina IRBM with
    range of 1,600 miles and a 2.3-megaton warhead
SS-5 – NATO's reporting name for R-14 Dvina IRBM with
    range of 2,200 miles and a 2.3-megaton warhead
SSU – Strategic Services Unit
TJ/kg – terajoule per kilogram – energy per unit of matter (T
    is 10 to the 12th power)
TNT –trinitrotoluene – chemical explosive 80 percent as
    powerful as dynamite, used to measure relative power of
    nuclear bombs
U-2 – U.S. Air Force jet used for spying on Soviet Union
U-235 – uranium isotope used in Little Boy bomb dropped
    on Hiroshima on August 6, 1945, with explosive
    equivalency of 15 kilotons
VADM – Vice Admiral
WADC – Wright Air Development Center
WSEG – Weapons Systems Evaluation Group
X-2 – counterespionage branch of the OSS that assisted Britain
    in World War II – led by James Murphy who discovered
    3,000 access agents and eliminated many of them

It is the author's intention to give proper credit to all sources. Philosophical and technical aspects of this book have been a learning experience for the author in philosophy, chemistry, and physics. The author has made efforts to be correct in all those subject matters but is not an expert in them. This book is about human existence, and those epistemologies are merely an adjunct to the story.

Bibliography

Helgerson, John L. "CIA Briefings of Presidential Candidates." CIABriefings. Accessed October 10, 2022. http://www.sacred-magick.com/free/files/ConspiracyArchives/CIA%20Briefings%20of%20Presidents.pdf.

Merlin, Peter W. *Unlimited Horizons: Design and Development of the U-2.* Washington, DC: National Aeronautics and Space Administration, 2015.

Pedlow, Gregory W., Donald E. Welzenbach, and Chris Pocock. *The Central Intelligence Agency and Overhead Reconnaissance: The U-2 and Oxcart Programs, 1954–1974.* New York: Simon and Schuster, 2016.

"Summary and Conclusions: 1958 Report of the Net Evaluation Subcommittee, National Security Council, 10 November 1958, Top Secret, Excised Copy." National Security Archive. Accessed October 10, 2022. https://nsarchive.gwu.edu/document/28613-document-5-summary-and-conclusions-1958-report-net-evaluation-subcommittee-national.

Endnotes

Chapter 2

[1] "1953, March 20, Nikita Khrushchev Begins His Rise to Power," History, accessed October 28, 2022, https://www.history.com/this-day-in-history/khrushchev-begins-his-rise-to-power.

[2] "1953, March 20, Nikita Khrushchev Begins His Rise to Power," History, accessed October 10, 2022, https://www.history.com/this-day-in-history/khrushchev-begins-his-rise-to-power.

[3] John L. Helgerson, "CIA Briefings of Presidential Candidates," CIA Briefings, accessed October 10, 2022, http://www.sacred-magick.com/free/files/ConspiracyArchives/CIA%20Briefings%20of%20Presidents.pdf.

[4] Letters between Truman and Eisenhower can be found online at Harry S. Truman Library and Museum, National Archives, https://www.trumanlibrary.gov/library/online-collections.

Chapter 3

[5] *Beacon Hill Report: Problems of Air Force Intelligence and Reconnaissance,* Project Lincoln: Massachusetts Institute of Technology, June 15, 1952, https://www.governmentattic.org/12docs/USAF-BeaconHillReport_1952.pdf.

Gregory W. Pedlow and Donald E. Welzenbach, *The Central Intelligence Agency and Overhead Reconnaissance: The U-2 and OXCART Programs, 1954–1974,* Washington, DC: History Staff, Central Intelligence Agency, 1992, https://documents.theblackvault.com/documents/ufos/CIAOverheadRecon-u2-oxcart.pdf.

[6] John L. Helgerson, "CIA Briefings of Presidential Candidates," CIA Briefings, accessed October 10, 2022, http://www.sacred-magick.com/free/files/ConspiracyArchives/CIA%20Briefings%20of%20Presidents.pdf.

[7] John L. Helgerson, "CIA Briefings of Presidential Candidates," CIA Briefings, accessed October 10, 2022, http://www.sacred-magick.com/free/files/ConspiracyArchives/CIA%20Briefings%20of%20Presidents.pdf.

[8] John L. Helgerson, "CIA Briefings of Presidential Candidates," CIA Briefings, accessed October 10, 2022, http://www.sacred-magick.com/free/files/ConspiracyArchives/CIA%20Briefings%20of%20Presidents.pdf.

[9] John L. Helgerson, "CIA Briefings of Presidential Candidates," CIA Briefings, accessed October 10, 2022, http://www.sacred-magick.com/free/files/ConspiracyArchives/CIA%20Briefings%20of%20Presidents.pdf.

Chapter 4

[10] John L. Helgerson, "CIA Briefings of Presidential Candidates," CIA Briefings, accessed October 10, 2022, http://www.sacred-magick.com/free/files/ConspiracyArchives/CIA%20Briefings%20of%20Presidents.pdf.

[11] John L. Helgerson, "CIA Briefings of Presidential Candidates," CIA Briefings, accessed October 10, 2022, http://www.sacred-magick.com/ free/files/ConspiracyArchives/CIA%20Briefings%20of%20Presidents.pdf.

[12] John L. Helgerson, "CIA Briefings of Presidential Candidates," CIA Briefings, accessed October 10, 2022, http://www.sacred-magick.com/ free/files/ConspiracyArchives/CIA%20Briefings%20of%20Presidents.pdf.

[13] John L. Helgerson, "CIA Briefings of Presidential Candidates," CIA Briefings, accessed October 10, 2022, http://www.sacred-magick.com/ free/files/ConspiracyArchives/CIA%20Briefings%20of%20Presidents.pdf.

Chapter 5

[14] *"Special National Intelligence Estimate 11-2-54,* 'Soviet Capabilities for Attack on the US through 1957,' TOP SECRET, 24 February 1954," National Security Archive, accessed October 10, 2022, https://nsarchive. gwu.edu/media/19832/ocr.

[15] *"Special National Intelligence Estimate 11-2-54,* 'Soviet Capabilities for Attack on the US through 1957,' TOP SECRET, 24 February 1954," National Security Archive, accessed October 10, 2022, https://nsarchive. gwu.edu/media/19832/ocr.

[16] *U.S. Air Force Project Rand Research Memorandum,* The RAND Corporation, accessed October 10, 2022, https://www.rand.org/content/ dam/rand/pubs/research_memoranda/2005/RM1166.pdf. "The Bomber Gap," GlobalSecurity.org, accessed October 10, 2022, https://www.globalsecurity.org/ wmd/world/russia/bomber-gap.htm.

[17] James Louis Isemann, "To Detect, to Deter, to Defend: The Distant Early Warning (DEW) Line and Early Cold War Defense Policy, 1953–1957" (dissertation, Kansas State University, 2009), accessed October 10, 2022, https://krex.k-state.edu/dspace/handle/2097/2161.

[18] David C. Elliot, "Project Vista and Nuclear Weapons in Europe," *International Security* 11, no. 1 (Summer, 1986), 163–183, https://doi.org/ 10.2307/2538879.

[19] T. D. Barnes, *CIA Station D: Area 51: The Complete Illustrated History of the CIA's Station D at Area 51* (University of Florida: Begell House, 2018).

[20] T. D. Barnes, *CIA Station D: Area 51: The Complete Illustrated History of the CIA's Station D at Area 51* (University of Florida: Begell House, 2018).

[21] The Air Research and Development Command that had its reconnaissance division in Baltimore, Maryland, headed by Lt. Col. Joseph J. Pellegrini, had to approve all new reconnaissance aircraft designs. Weapons and Warfare: History and Hardware of Warfare, accessed October 10, 2022, https://weapons andwarfare.com/category/ air-warfare/page/49/.

[22] *The Central Intelligence Agency and Overhead Reconnaissance: The U-2 and OXCART Programs, 1954–1974*, Washington, DC: History Staff, Central

Intelligence Agency, 1992, https://documents.theblackvault.com/documents/ufos/CIAOverheadRecon-u2-oxcart.pdf.

[23] Cambridge Dictionary, accessed October 10, 2022, https://dictionary.cambridge.org/us/dictionary/english/in-the-country-of-the-blind-the-one-eyed-man-is-king.

Chapter 6

[24] *History of the Joint Chiefs of Staff: The Joint Chiefs of Staff and National Policy 1953–1954*, accessed October 10, 2022, https://archive.org/stream/historyofjointch05schn/historyofjointch05schn_djvu.txt.

[25] Robert J. Watson, *The Joint Chiefs of Staff and National Policy 1953–1954*, History of the Joint Chiefs of Staff, Volume V, accessed October 10, 2022, https://archive.org/stream/historyofjointch05schn/historyofjointch05schn_djvu.txt.

[26] *History of the Joint Chiefs of Staff: The Joint Chiefs of Staff and National Policy 1953–1954*, accessed December 8, 2022, https://archive.org/stream/historyofjointch05schn/ historyofjointch05schn_djvu.txt.

[27] *History of the Joint Chiefs of Staff: The Joint Chiefs of Staff and National Policy 1953–1954*, accessed December 8, 2022, https://archive.org/stream/historyofjointch05schn/ historyofjointch05schn_djvu.txt.

[28] Sean M. Maloney, *Emergency War Plan: The American Doomsday Machine, 1945–1960* (Lincoln, NE: Potomac Books, 2021).

[29] *History of the Joint Chiefs of Staff: The Joint Chiefs of Staff and National Policy 1953–1954*, accessed December 8, 2022, https://archive.org/stream/historyofjointch05schn/ historyofjointch05schn_djvu.txt.

[30] James Louis Isemann, "To Detect, to Deter, to Defend: The Distant Early Warning (DEW) Line and Early Cold War Defense Policy, 1953–1957," https://krex.k-state.edu/dspace/handle/2097/2161. *History of the Joint Chiefs of Staff: The Joint Chiefs of Staff and National Policy 1953–1954*, accessed December 8, 2022, https://archive.org/stream/historyofjointch05schn/ historyofjointch05schn_djvu.txt.

[31] *History of the Joint Chiefs of Staff: The Joint Chiefs of Staff and National Policy 1953–1954*, accessed December 8, 2022, https://archive.org/stream/historyofjointch05schn/ historyofjointch05schn_djvu.txt.

[32] *History of the Joint Chiefs of Staff: The Joint Chiefs of Staff and National Policy 1953–1954*, accessed December 8, 2022, https://archive.org/stream/historyofjointch05schn/ historyofjointch05schn_djvu.txt.

[33] *History of the Joint Chiefs of Staff: The Joint Chiefs of Staff and National Policy 1953–1954*, accessed December 8, 2022, https://archive.org/stream/historyofjointch05schn/ historyofjointch05schn_djvu.txt.

[34] *History of the Joint Chiefs of Staff: The Joint Chiefs of Staff and National Policy 1953–1954*, accessed December 8, 2022, https://archive.org/stream/historyofjointch05schn/ historyofjointch05schn_djvu.txt.

[35] "Project Solarium," Wikipedia, accessed October 11, 2022, https://en.wikipedia.org/wiki/Project_ Solarium.

[36] "Project Solarium," Wikipedia, accessed October 11, 2022, https://en.wikipedia.org/wiki/Project_ Solarium.

[37] Marc Trachtenberg, "A 'Wasting Asset': American Strategy and the Shifting Nuclear Balance," *International Security* 13, No. 3 (Winter 1988/1989): 39–40. https://doi.org/10.2307/2538735.

[38] "The East German Uprising, 1953," Department of State, Office of the Historian, accessed October 11, 2022, https://history.state.gov/milestones/1953-1960/east-german-uprising#:~:text=On%20June%2016%2C%201953%2C%20workers,East%20German%20cities%20and%20towns.

Chapter 7

[39] "The East German Uprising, 1953," Department of State, Office of the Historian, accessed October 11, 2022, https://history.state.gov/milestones/1953-1960/east-german-uprising#:~:text=On%20June%2016%2C%201953%2C%20workers,East%20German%20cities%20and%20towns.

[40] Jim Dankiewicz, "The East German Uprising of June 17, 1953, and Its Effects on the USSR and Other Nations of Eastern Europe" (research paper, University of California, Santa Barbara, 1999), https://marcuse.faculty.history.ucsb.edu/classes/133p/133p99/jim1953.993.htm.

[41] Jim Dankiewicz, "The East German Uprising of June 17, 1953, and Its Effects on the USSR and Other Nations of Eastern Europe" (research paper, University of California, Santa Barbara, 1999), https://marcuse.faculty.history.ucsb.edu/classes/133p/133p99/jim1953.993.htm.

[42] "No provocateur of any nationality can persuade human beings to stand up in front of rumbling tanks with sticks and stones." Quoted in Jim Dankiewicz, "The East German Uprising of June 17, 1953, and Its Effects on the USSR and Other Nations of Eastern Europe" (research paper, University of California, Santa Barbara, 1999), https://marcuse.faculty.history.ucsb.edu/classes/133p/133p99/jim1953.993.htm.

Chapter 8

[43] Paul Glenshaw, "Secret Casualties of the Cold War," *Smithsonian Air & Space Magazine*, December 2017, https://www.smithsonianmag.com/air-space-magazine/secret-casualties-of-the-cold-war-180967122/.

[44] T. D. Barnes, *CIA Station D: Area 51: The Complete Illustrated History of the CIA's Station D at Area 51* (University of Florida: Begell House, 2018).

[45] "Spies: The U.S. and Russian Espionage Game from the Cold War to the 21st Century," EBIN, accessed October 11, 2022, https://ebin.pub/spies-the-us-and-russian-espionage-game-from-the-cold-war-to-the-21st-century-1440840423-9781440840425.html.

[46] Gregory W. Pedlow and Donald E. Welzenbach, *The Central Intelligence Agency and Overhead Reconnaissance: The U-2 and OXCART Programs, 1954–1974*, Washington, DC: History Staff, Central Intelligence Agency, 1992, https://documents.theblackvault.com/documents/ufos/CIAOverheadRecon-u2-oxcart.pdf.

[47] Gregory W. Pedlow and Donald E. Welzenbach, *The Central Intelligence Agency and Overhead Reconnaissance: The U-2 and OXCART Programs, 1954–1974*, Washington, DC: History Staff, Central Intelligence Agency, 1992, https://documents.theblackvault.com/documents/ufos/CIAOverheadRecon-u2-oxcart.pdf.

[48] Weapons and Warfare: History and Hardware of Warfare, accessed October 10, 2022, https://weaponsandwarfare.com/category/air-warfare/page/49/.

Chapter 9

[49] "Full Text of 'CIA UFO Documents,'" Internet Archive, accessed October 11, 2022, https://archive.org/stream/CIAUFO/THE%20CENTRAL%20INTELLIGENCE%20AGENCY%20AND%20OVERHEAD%20RECONNAISSANCE%3B%20THE%20U-2%20AND%20OXCART%20PROGRAMS%2C%201954-1974_djvu.txt.

[50] Gregory W. Pedlow and Donald E. Welzenbach, *The Central Intelligence Agency and Overhead Reconnaissance: The U-2 and OXCART Programs, 1954–1974*, Washington, DC: History Staff, Central Intelligence Agency, 1992, https://documents.theblackvault.com/documents/ufos/CIAOverheadRecon-u2-oxcart.pdf.

[51] Peter W. Merlin, *Unlimited Horizons: Design and Development of the U-2*. Washington, DC: National Aeronautics and Space Administration, 2015. https://www.scribd.com/document/335609696/unlimited-horizons-pdf.

[52] Peter W. Merlin, *Unlimited Horizons: Design and Development of the U-2*. Washington, DC: National Aeronautics and Space Administration, 2015. https://www.scribd.com/document/335609696/unlimited-horizons-pdf.

[53] Peter W. Merlin, *Unlimited Horizons: Design and Development of the U-2*. Washington, DC: National Aeronautics and Space Administration, 2015. https://www.scribd.com/document/335609696/unlimited-horizons-pdf.

[54] Peter W. Merlin, *Unlimited Horizons: Design and Development of the U-2*. Washington, DC: National Aeronautics and Space Administration, 2015. https://www.scribd.com/document/335609696/unlimited-horizons-pdf.

[55] Peter W. Merlin, *Unlimited Horizons: Design and Development of the U-2*. Washington, DC: National Aeronautics and Space Administration, 2015. https://www.scribd.com/document/335609696/unlimited-horizons-pdf.

Chapter 10

[56] Peter W. Merlin, *Unlimited Horizons: Design and Development of the U-2*. Washington, DC: National Aeronautics and Space Administration,

2015. http://docshare.tips/unlimited-horizonspdf_58a8acd9b6d87f126 f8b4f6c.html.

[57] Peter W. Merlin, *Unlimited Horizons: Design and Development of the U-2*. Washington, DC: National Aeronautics and Space Administration, 2015. http://docshare.tips/unlimited-horizonspdf_58a8acd9b6d87f126 f8b4f6c.html.

[58] Peter W. Merlin, *Unlimited Horizons: Design and Development of the U-2*. Washington, DC: National Aeronautics and Space Administration, 2015, http://docshare.tips/unlimited-horizonspdf_58a8acd9b6d87f126 f8b4f6c.html.

[59] Peter W. Merlin, *Unlimited Horizons: Design and Development of the U-2*. Washington, DC: National Aeronautics and Space Administration, 2015, http://docshare.tips/unlimited-horizonspdf_58a8acd9b6d87f126 f8b4f6c.html.

[60] Gregory W. Pedlow and Donald E. Welzenbach, *The Central Intelligence Agency and Overhead Reconnaissance: The U-2 and OXCART Programs, 1954–1974*, Washington, DC: History Staff, Central Intelligence Agency, 1992, https://documents.theblackvault.com/documents/ufos/ CIAOverheadRecon-u2-oxcart.pdf.

[61] Gregory W. Pedlow and Donald E. Welzenbach, *The Central Intelligence Agency and Overhead Reconnaissance: The U-2 and OXCART Programs, 1954–1974*, Washington, DC: History Staff, Central Intelligence Agency, 1992, https://documents.theblackvault.com/documents/ufos/ CIAOverheadRecon-u2-oxcart.pdf.

Chapter 11

[62] "The Determinants of the Dutch Demand for Military Spending," DocPlayer, accessed October 11, 2022, http://docplayer.net/40598817- Title-the-determinants-of-the-dutch-demand-for-military-spending.html.

Chapter 12

[63] Since the CL-282 was designed for a maneuvering load factor of 2.5Gs compared to 7.33Gs on the XF-104, fuselage strength requirements were reduced, allowing for reduced material gauges. Peter W. Merlin, *Unlimited Horizons: Design and Development of the U-2*. Washington, DC: National Aeronautics and Space Administration, 2015, http://docshare. tips/unlimited-horizonspdf_58a8acd9b6d87f126f8b4f6c. html.

[64] Skid plates on the wingtips protected the airfoils during landing. Peter W. Merlin, *Unlimited Horizons: Design and Development of the U-2*. Washington, DC: National Aeronautics and Space Administration, 2015, http://docshare.tips/unlimited-horizonspdf_58a8acd9b6d87f126 f8b4f6c.html.

[65] Gregory W. Pedlow and Donald E. Welzenbach, *The Central Intelligence Agency and Overhead Reconnaissance: The U-2 and OXCART Programs, 1954–1974*, Washington, DC: History Staff, Central Intelligence

Agency, 1992, https://documents.theblackvault.com/documents/ufos/CIAOverheadRecon-u2-oxcart.pdf.

[66] Peter W. Merlin, *Unlimited Horizons: Design and Development of the U-2*. Washington, DC: National Aeronautics and Space Administration, 2015, http://docshare.tips/unlimited-horizonspdf_58a8acd9b6d87f126f8b4f6c.html.

Chapter 13

[67] Project Aquatone was a covert operation; therefore, a "cover story" was required. On May 7, 1956, the National Advisory Committee for Aeronautics (NACA, the predecessor of NASA) issued a press release that described the U-2 as an aeronautical research aircraft capable of reaching 55,000 feet. NACA would be flying it in the United States and from US airbases abroad. Gregory W. Pedlow and Donald E. Welzenbach, *The Central Intelligence Agency and Overhead Reconnaissance: The U-2 and OXCART Programs, 1954–1974*, Washington, DC: History Staff, Central Intelligence Agency, 1992, https://documents.theblackvault.com/documents/ufos/CIAOverheadRecon-u2-oxcart.pdf.

[68] Gregory W. Pedlow and Donald E. Welzenbach, *The Central Intelligence Agency and Overhead Reconnaissance: The U-2 and OXCART Programs, 1954–1974*, Washington, DC: History Staff, Central Intelligence Agency, 1992, https://documents.theblackvault.com/documents/ufos/CIAOverheadRecon-u2-oxcart.pdf.

[69] Gregory W. Pedlow and Donald E. Welzenbach, *The Central Intelligence Agency and Overhead Reconnaissance: The U-2 and OXCART Programs, 1954–1974*, Washington, DC: History Staff, Central Intelligence Agency, 1992, https://documents.theblackvault.com/documents/ufos/CIAOverheadRecon-u2-oxcart.pdf.

[70] Before U-2 operations began, the CIA's Office of Scientific Intelligence (OSI) conducted a vulnerability study of the U-2 that was published on May 28, 1956. The study's conclusion was that "maximum Soviet radar detection ranges against the Project aircraft at elevation in excess of 55,000 feet would vary from 20 to 150 miles. . . . In our opinion, detection can therefore be assumed." The OSI study added, "It is doubtful that the Soviets can achieve consistent tracking of the Project vehicle." It was completed just three weeks before the initiation of overflights. "CIA Report That Reveals 'Area 51,'" SCRIBD, accessed October 11, 2022, https://www.scribd.com/doc/160716580/CIA-Report-That-Reveals-Area-51.

Chapter 14

[71] This procedure was known as pre-breathing. During high-altitude cruise, the cabin-pressure altitude was maintained between 28,000 and 30,000 feet. The pilot's suit automatically pressurized to 3 psi because breathing pure oxygen at 3 psi at 29,000 feet is equivalent to breathing

ambient air at sea level. Without pressurized oxygen, the time of useful consciousness at 70,000 feet is only a few seconds. Peter W. Merlin, *Unlimited Horizons: Design and Development of the U-2*. Washington, DC: National Aeronautics and Space Administration, 2015, http://docshare. tips/unlimited-horizonspdf_58a8acd9b6d87f126f8b4f6c. html.

[72] Peter W. Merlin, *Unlimited Horizons: Design and Development of the U-2*. Washington, DC: National Aeronautics and Space Administration, 2015, http://docshare.tips/unlimited-horizonspdf_ 58a8acd9b6d87f126f8b4f6c.html.

[73] Gregory W. Pedlow and Donald E. Welzenbach, *The Central Intelligence Agency and Overhead Reconnaissance: The U-2 and OXCART Programs, 1954–1974*, Washington, DC: History Staff, Central Intelligence Agency, 1992, https://documents.theblackvault.com/documents/ufos/ CIAOverheadRecon-u2-oxcart.pdf.

[74] He quickly flew to Bonn with CIA Deputy Director Pierre Cabell. Contrary to their fears, the "Iron Chancellor" proved to be enthusiastic about the project. As Bissell later recalled, Adenauer exclaimed, "This is a wonderful idea. It's just what ought to be done!" Gregory W. Pedlow and Donald E. Welzenbach, *The Central Intelligence Agency and Overhead Reconnaissance: The U-2 and OXCART Programs, 1954–1974*, Washington, DC: History Staff, Central Intelligence Agency, 1992, https:// documents.theblackvault.com/documents/ufos/CIAOverheadRecon- u2-oxcart.pdf.

Chapter 15

[75] Alexander Orlov, "The U-2 Program: A Russian Officer Remembers," A "Hot" Front in the Cold War, accessed October 11, 2022, http://web. archive.org/web/20060713154414/http:/www.cia.gov/csi/studies/ winter98_99/art02.html.

[76] T. D. Barnes, *CIA Station D: Area 51: The Complete Illustrated History of the CIA's Station D at Area 51* (University of Florida: Begell House, 2018).

[77] Gregory W. Pedlow and Donald E. Welzenbach, *The Central Intelligence Agency and Overhead Reconnaissance: The U-2 and OXCART Programs, 1954–1974*, Washington, DC: History Staff, Central Intelligence Agency, 1992, https://documents.theblackvault.com/documents/ufos/ CIAOverheadRecon-u2-oxcart.pdf.

[78] Gregory W. Pedlow and Donald E. Welzenbach, *The Central Intelligence Agency and Overhead Reconnaissance: The U-2 and OXCART Programs, 1954–1974*, Washington, DC: History Staff, Central Intelligence Agency, 1992, https://documents.theblackvault.com/documents/ufos/ CIAOverheadRecon-u2-oxcart.pdf.

[79] Gregory W. Pedlow and Donald E. Welzenbach, *The Central Intelligence Agency and Overhead Reconnaissance: The U-2 and OXCART*

Programs, 1954–1974, Washington, DC: History Staff, Central Intelligence Agency, 1992, https://documents.theblackvault.com/documents/ufos/CIAOverheadRecon-u2-oxcart.pdf.

[80] Gregory W. Pedlow and Donald E. Welzenbach, *The Central Intelligence Agency and Overhead Reconnaissance: The U-2 and OXCART Programs, 1954–1974,* Washington, DC: History Staff, Central Intelligence Agency, 1992, https://documents.theblackvault.com/documents/ufos/CIAOverheadRecon-u2-oxcart.pdf.

[81] Peter W. Merlin, *Unlimited Horizons: Design and Development of the U-2.* Washington, DC: National Aeronautics and Space Administration, 2015, http://docshare.tips/unlimited-horizonspdf_58a8acd9b6d87f126f8b4f6c.html.

Chapter 16

[82] Quotes from diplomatic messages. Helen H. Kleyla, "Full Text of 'History of the Office of Special Activities from Inception to 1969,'" Internet Archive, May 1974, https://archive.org/stream/History OfTheOfficeOfSpecialActivitiesFromInceptionTo1969/Directorate OfScienceTechnologydstHistoryOfTheOfficeOfSpecialActivitiesosa FromInceptionTo1969_djvu.txt.

Chapter 18

[83] In 1950, Britain, France, and the United States issued a Tripartite Declaration in which they agreed to take action to prevent any violation of the 1947 armistice lines separating Israel from its Arab neighbors. Intended to defuse the situation, the declaration did little to calm tensions, but it did become a central factor in Washington, DC, policymaking. Gregory W. Pedlow and Donald E. Welzenbach, *The Central Intelligence Agency and Overhead Reconnaissance: The U-2 and OXCART Programs, 1954–1974,* Washington, DC: History Staff, Central Intelligence Agency, 1992, https://documents.theblack vault.com/documents/ufos/CIAOverheadRecon-u2-oxcart.pdf.

[84] Gregory W. Pedlow and Donald E. Welzenbach, *The Central Intelligence Agency and Overhead Reconnaissance: The U-2 and OXCART Programs, 1954–1974,* Washington, DC: History Staff, Central Intelligence Agency, 1992, https://documents.theblackvault.com/documents/ufos/CIAOverheadRecon-u2-oxcart.pdf.

Peter W. Merlin, *Unlimited Horizons: Design and Development of the U-2.* Washington, DC: National Aeronautics and Space Administration, 2015, http://docshare.tips/unlimited-horizonspdf_58a8acd9b6d87f1 26f8b4f6c.html; and Editors of Encyclopaedia Britannica, *Suez Crisis,* Britannica, accessed October 11, 2022, https://www.britannica.com/event/Suez-Crisis.

Chapter 19

[85] An issue that has preoccupied scholars is Nagy's declaration of neutrality and withdrawal from the Warsaw Pact and the Soviet decision to invade Hungary. Did Nagy's declaration provoke the second Soviet attack, or had the Kremlin leaders already decided to intervene? Johanna Granville, "The First Domino – Int'l Decision Making during Hungary 1956," SCRIBD, accessed October 11, 2022, scribd.com/doc/144894637/The-First-Domino-Int-l-Decision-Making-During-Hungary-1956-Johanna-Granville.

Chapter 20

[86] Malenkov, Molotov, Saburov, Khrushchev, Brezhnev, Zhukov, Shvernik, Shepilov, Furtseva, Pospelov, and Zorin on the situation in Hungary. "Soviets Put a Brutal End to Hungarian Revolution," This Day in History November 04, 1956, History, accessed October 11, 2022, https://www.history.com/this-day-in-history/soviets-put-brutal-end-to-hungarian-revolution.

Helen H. Kleyla, "Full Text of 'History of the Office of Special Activities from Inception to 1969,'" Internet Archive, May 1974, https://archive.org/stream/HistoryOfTheOfficeOfSpecialActivitiesFromInceptionTo1969/DirectorateOfScienceTechnologydstHistoryOfTheOfficeOfSpecialActivitiesosaFromInceptionTo1969_djvu.txt.

"Hungarian Revolution of 1956," New World Encyclopedia, accessed October 11, 2022, https://www.newworldencyclopedia.org/entry/Hungarian_Revolution_of_1956.

Martin Ivan Elzy, "American Governmental Response to the 1956 Hungarian Revolution" (thesis, Eastern Illinois University, 1999), https://thekeep.eiu.edu/cgi/viewcontent.ci?amp=&article= 5083&context=theses.

[87] "Hungarian Revolution of 1956," Wikipedia, accessed October 11, 2022, https://en.wikipedia.org/wiki/ Hungarian_Revolution_of_1956.

Chapter 21

[88] Martin Ivan Elzy, "American Governmental Response to the 1956 Hungarian Revolution" (thesis, Eastern Illinois University, 1999), https://thekeep.eiu.edu/cgi/viewcontent.cgi?amp=&article =5083&context=theses.

Chapter 22

[89] Speech to Western diplomats at reception in Moscow for Polish leader Mr. Gomulka, November 18, 1956. "Foreign News: We Will Bury You!" *Time*, November 26, 1956, https://content.time.com/time/ subscriber/article/0,33009,867329,00.html.

[90] President Eisenhower had approved the mission after being told by the Air Force that the high-speed RB-57Ds would probably not be detected. "Full Text of 'CIA UFO Documents,'" Internet Archive, accessed October 11, 2022, https://archive.org/stream/CIAUFO/THE%20

CENTRAL%20INTELLIGENCE%20AGENCY%20AND%20
OVERHEAD%20RECONNAISSANCE%3B%20THE%20U-2%20
AND%20OXCART%20PROGRAMS%2C%201954-1974_djvu.txt.

[91] Peter W. Merlin, *Unlimited Horizons: Design and Development of the U-2*. Washington, DC: National Aeronautics and Space Administration, 2015, http://docshare.tips/unlimited-horizonspdf_58a8acd9b6d87f126f8b 4f6c.html.

Chapter 23

[92] "Message to First Pugwash Conference," in *The Collected Papers of Bertrand Russell, Volume 29* (New York: Routledge, 2005), https:// www.taylorfrancis.com/chapters/mono/10.4324/9780203004555-78/ message-first-pugwash-conference-1957-bertrand-russell-andrew-bone.

[93] Leticia Gaspar, "Spatial Distribution of Fallout and Lithogenic Radionuclides Controlled by Soil Carbon and Water Erosion in an Agroforestry South-Pyrenean Catchment," *Journal of Medical Physics and Applied Sciences* 6, no. 3 (2021), https://medicalphysics.imedpub.com/ spatial-distribution-of-fallout-and-lithogenic-radionuclides-controlled-by-soil-carbon-and-water-erosion-in-an-agroforestry-southp.pdf. Whether it emits alpha or beta particles, gamma rays, X-rays, or neutrons, a quantity of radioactive material is expressed in terms of its radioactivity (or simply its activity), which represents how many atoms in the material decay in a given time period. The units of measure for radioactivity are the curie (Ci) and becquerel (Bq). Exposure describes the amount of radiation traveling through the air. Many radiation monitors measure exposure. "Radiation Units, Measurement and Dosimetry," Medical Diagnostic Imaging Science, Course Hero, accessed October 11, 2022, https://www.coursehero.com/file/133790760/RADIATION-UNITS-AND-MEASUREMENTdocx/.

[94] The rad is a unit of absorbed radiation dose, defined as 1 rad = 0.01 Gy = 0.01 J/kg. It was originally defined in CGS units in 1953 as the dose causing 100 ergs of energy to be absorbed by one gram of matter. The material absorbing the radiation can be human tissue or silicon microchips or any other medium (for example, air, water, lead shielding, etc.). "Rad (unit)," Wikipedia, accessed October 11, 2022, https:// en.wikipedia.org/wiki/Rad_%28unit%29. To cause biological damage; it describes the physiological effects of a given radiation type (i.e., gamma, neutron, alpha and beta) in relation to the amount of the type of radiation absorbed. For beta and gamma radiation, the dose equivalent is the same as the absorbed dose. So 1 rad = 1 rem. By contrast, the dose equivalent is larger than the absorbed dose for alpha and neutron radiation because these types of radiation are more damaging to the human body. "State of Connecticut Radiation

Professional Volunteer Program (CT-RPVP)," SlidePlayer, accessed October 11, 2022, http://slideplayer.com/slide/2522172/.

Chapter 25

[95] David L. Snead, "The Gaither Committee, Eisenhower, and the Cold War," Knowledge Bank, 1999, https://kb.osu.edu/handle/1811/31710.

[96] James Killian TCP quote. David L. Snead, "The Gaither Committee, Eisenhower, and the Cold War," Knowledge Bank, 1999, https://kb.osu.edu/handle/1811/31710.

[97] David Lindsey Snead, *Eisenhower and the Gaither Report: The Influences of a Committee of Experts on National Security Policy in the Late 1950s* (dissertation, University of Virginia, January 1997), https://digitalcommons.liberty.edu/cgi/viewcontent.cgi?referer=&httpsredir=1&article=1056&context=fac_dis.

[98] David L. Snead, "The Gaither Committee, Eisenhower, and the Cold War," p. 68, Knowledge Bank, 1999, https://kb.osu.edu/handle/1811/31710.

[99] David L. Snead, "The Gaither Committee, Eisenhower, and the Cold War," p. 70, Knowledge Bank, 1999, https://kb.osu.edu/handle/1811/31710.

[100] One strategic option envisioned the United States initiating a war with the Soviet Union. On at least two other occasions, the commanders discussed preventive and preemptive attacks. David L. Snead, "The Gaither Committee, Eisenhower, and the Cold War," p. 86, Knowledge Bank, 1999, https://kb.osu.edu/handle/1811/31710.

[101] LeMay's views: agreement at the top governmental level that when such information is received the Strategic Air Command will be directed to attack. He reiterated this strategy in a lecture at the National War College in 1954. LeMay's views are important because they shed light on a debate that was raging among Air Force commanders and because he was an influential witness before the Gaither Committee. David L. Snead, "The Gaither Committee, Eisenhower, and the Cold War," Knowledge Bank, 1999, https://kb.osu.edu/handle/1811/31710.

[102] "Sprague Interview," OpenVault, accessed October 11, 2022, https://openvault.wgbh.org/transcripts/V_C37CC19886C0489E9E03B58A7A151E33.

[103] "Sprague Interview," OpenVault, accessed October 11, 2022, https://openvault.wgbh.org/transcripts/V_C37CC19886C0489E9E03B58A7A151E33.

[104] "Sprague Interview," OpenVault, accessed October 11, 2022, https://openvault.wgbh.org/transcripts/ V_C37CC19886C0489E9E03B58A7A151E33.

[105] "I think I suffered for about a minute, not more than 2 minutes, with the perspiration running down my face when I finally said, 'Mr. President I don't think Mr. Foster and I can contribute any more to this meeting. And I'd like permission to leave.' He didn't even respond to

that. So without waiting more than about 15 seconds, I got up, walked out, Foster followed me and that was the end of the meeting." "Sprague Interview," OpenVault, accessed October 11, 2022, https://openvault. wgbh.org/transcripts/ V_C37CC19886C0489E9E03B58A7A151E33.

Chapter 26

[106] "Alsop used the occasion to renew his charges that 'the present American air defense is totally inadequate to prevent a devastating attack by the growing Soviet air and missile forces.'" Morton H. Halperin, *World Politics* (Vol. 13) (New York: Cambridge University Press, 1961), 360–384.

[107] The *Washington Post* reprinted this in Arnold L. Norelick, *Strategic Power and Soviet Foreign Policy* (Chicago: University of Chicago Press, 1966), 48. Pravada, November 29, 1957, reprinted in Arnold L. Norelick, *Strategic Power and Soviet Foreign Policy* (Chicago: University of Chicago Press, 1966), 44– 45. It finds America's long-term prospect one of cataclysmic peril in the face of rocketing Soviet military might and of a powerful, growing Soviet economy and technology, which will bring new political propaganda and psychological assaults on freedom all around the globe. Public knowledge of the report made the administration's evaluations more difficult. As an internal document, Eisenhower and his advisers had great freedom in assessing the report's worth.

[108] David L. Snead, "The Gaither Committee, Eisenhower, and the Cold War," p. 138, Knowledge Bank, 1999, https://kb.osu.edu/handle/1811/31710.

[109] David L. Snead, "The Gaither Committee, Eisenhower, and the Cold War," Knowledge Bank, 1999, https://kb.osu.edu/handle/1811/31710.

[110] David L. Snead, "The Gaither Committee, Eisenhower, and the Cold War," Knowledge Bank, 1999, https://kb.osu.edu/handle/1811/31710.

[111] One of the last Gaither Committee recommendations concerned augmentation of United States' limited military operations capabilities. David L. Snead, "The Gaither Committee, Eisenhower, and the Cold War," Knowledge Bank, 1999, https://kb.osu.edu/handle/1811/31710.

[112] Although contained in presidential directive, NSC 5816 has further disclosure about NESC. "Memorandum of Discussion at the 442d Meeting of the National Security Council," Department of State, Office of the Historian, April 28, 1960, https://history.state.gov/historicaldocuments/frus1958-60v03/d97.

[113] In November 1957, Khrushchev gave two seemingly threatening interviews. He argued, "If war is not averted, the Americans will experience the most devastating war ever known to mankind. It will rage not only in Europe and Asia, but, with not less fury, in the United States." A little over a week later, he bragged, "The fact that the Soviet Union was the first to launch an artificial earth satellite, which within

a month was followed by another." David L. Snead, "The Gaither Committee, Eisenhower, and the Cold War," Knowledge Bank, 1999, https://kb.osu.edu/handle/1811/31710.

[114] Though the Soviets' SS-6 Sapwood missile program was actually stalled due to technical failures, subsequent boasts—and U.S. Secretary of Defense Neil McElroy's statement in February 1959 to Congress that the Soviets might have a three-to-one temporary advantage in ICBMs during the early 1960s—caused widespread concern in the United States about the existence of a "missile gap." The American intelligence community was divided, with the CIA suspecting technical delays. David L. Snead, "The Gaither Committee, Eisenhower, and the Cold War," Knowledge Bank, 1999, https://www.jstor.org/stable/2147598.

Chapter 29

[115] Liubov Zatsepina, "Competition, Masculinities, and Peacekeeping: Constructions of Soviet Nuclear Identity and Policy from Stalin to Gorbachev" (thesis, The University of Edinburgh), accessed October 11, 2022, https://era.ed.ac.uk/bitstream/handle/1842/37334/Zatsepina2020.pdf?isAllowed=y& sequence=1.

[116] Gregory W. Pedlow and Donald E. Welzenbach, *The Central Intelligence Agency and Overhead Reconnaissance: The U-2 and OXCART Programs, 1954–1974*, Washington, DC: History Staff, Central Intelligence Agency, 1992, https://documents.theblackvault.com/documents/ufos/CIAOverheadRecon-u2-oxcart.pdf.

Prime Minister Macmillan: "On 5 February 1960, a Detachment B U-2C with squadron leader John MacArthur at the controls left Peshawar, Pakistan, to conduct Operation KNIFE EDGE. The plane overflew the Tyuratam Missile Test Range, headed northwest to Kazan, and then turned south, photographing long stretches of the Soviet rail network. The excellent photography from this mission did not reveal a single missile site." Gregory W. Pedlow and Donald E. Welzenbach, *The Central Intelligence Agency and Overhead Reconnaissance: The U-2 and OXCART Programs, 1954–1974*, Washington, DC: History Staff, Central Intelligence Agency, 1992, https://documents.theblackvault.com/documents/ ufos/CIAOverheadRecon-u2-oxcart.pdf .

[117] Nikita S. Khrushchev, *Khrushchev Remembers: The Last Testament* (Boston: Little, Brown, & Co., 1974), 44.

Gregory W. Pedlow and Donald E. Welzenbach, *The Central Intelligence Agency and Overhead Reconnaissance: The U-2 and OXCART Programs, 1954–1974*, Washington, DC: History Staff, Central Intelligence Agency, 1992, https://documents.theblackvault.com/documents/ufos/CIAOverheadRecon-u2-oxcart.pdf.

[118] "The entire overflight lasted more than six hours. Following this incident, the Soviet leadership appointed a commission that included

the author of this article--who at that time was serving on the Main Staff of the Air Defense Forces--to investigate the reasons for the failure of the Air and Air Defense forces to move successfully against the aircraft that had violated Soviet airspace for so many hours. The investigation uncovered serious shortcomings in air combat training and in command and control of Air Defense and Air Force personnel and weapons systems. Many omissions were discovered in the operation of advanced radio equipment. In particular, information related to this reconnaissance activity had been acquired by Soviet communications interception facilities in the Transcaucasus several days before it happened, but the information was not reported to the command element because of a number of chance happenings. Khrushchev was indignant. Reality had undercut his repeated statements about the high degree of Soviet combat readiness." Alexander Orlov, "The U-2 Program: A Russian Officer Remembers," A "Hot" Front in the Cold War, accessed October 11, 2022, http://web.archive.org/web/20060713154414/http:/www.cia.gov/csi/studies/winter98_99/art02.html.

Chapter 30
[119] Dario Leone, "History, Explained: How Russia Shot Down a U-2 Spy Plane," The National Interest, August 5, 2019, https://nationalinterest.org/blog/buzz/history-explained-how-russia-shot-down-u-2-spy-plane-71546. "Debriefing of Francis Gary Powers, February 1962," All World Wars, accessed October 28, 2022, http://www.allworldwars.com/Debriefing-of-Francis-Gary-Powers.html.

[120] Boris Egorov, "How an Elusive U.S. Spy Plane Was Shot Down over the USSR," Russia Beyond, accessed October 11, 2022, https://www.rbth.com/history/335131-elusive-us-spy-plane-ussr. Ron Capshaw, "Interview with Francis Gary Powers, Jr.," Law & Liberty, October 9, 2015, https://lawliberty.org/interview-with-francis-gary-powers-jr/.

Chapter 31
[121] Khrushchev said that unless Eisenhower met these conditions, "the Soviet government sees no possibility of fruitful negotiations." Jack M. Schick, The Berlin Crisis 1958–1962 (Philadelphia: University of Pennsylvania Press, 1971), http://web.stanford.edu/group/tomzgroup/pmwiki/uploads/0253-1971-Schick-JHS.pdf.

[122] Western participants at the meeting said he seemed self-conscious about Malinovsky's presence. Jack M. Schick, The Berlin Crisis 1958–1962 (Philadelphia: University of Pennsylvania Press, 1971), http://web.stanford.edu/group/tomzgroup/pmwiki/uploads/0253-1971-Schick-JHS.pdf.

[123] De Gaulle reminded Khrushchev that espionage by aerial means included Soviet satellites passing over France. At that remark, Khrushchev

declared: "As God is my witness, my hands are clean, and my soul is pure." In the ensuing discussion, Khrushchev queried, "What the devil pushed these people to fly over the Soviet Union?" De Gaulle replied, "There are many devils in the world and we are here precisely for that reason. Jack M. Schick, *The Berlin Crisis 1958–1962* (Philadelphia: University of Pennsylvania Press, 1971), http://web.stanford.edu/group/tomzgroup/pmwiki/uploads/0253-1971-Schick-JHS.pdf.

Made in the USA
Monee, IL
09 April 2024

56172876R00148